Tales from Oscar Wilde

Retold by Stephanie Laslett

PARRAGON

A Parragon Book

Published by
Parragon Publishing,
Queen Street House, 4 Queen Street,
Bath BA1 1HE

Produced by
The Templar Company plc,
Pippbrook Mill, London Road, Dorking,
Surrey RH4 1JE

Printed and bound in China.
ISBN 0 75253 148 4

Contents

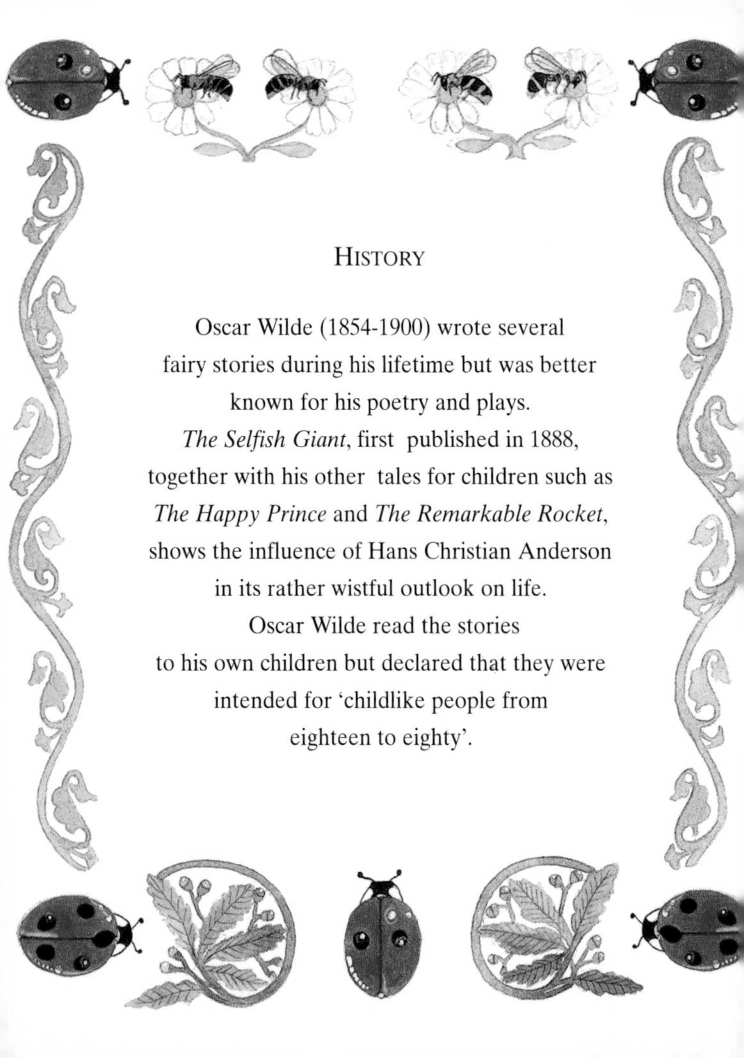

History

Oscar Wilde (1854-1900) wrote several
fairy stories during his lifetime but was better
known for his poetry and plays.
The Selfish Giant, first published in 1888,
together with his other tales for children such as
The Happy Prince and *The Remarkable Rocket*,
shows the influence of Hans Christian Anderson
in its rather wistful outlook on life.
Oscar Wilde read the stories
to his own children but declared that they were
intended for 'childlike people from
eighteen to eighty'.

The Selfish Giant

Every afternoon on their way home from school, the children used to go and play together in the Giant's garden.

It was a large lovely garden, with soft green grass. Here and there beautiful flowers like stars stood gently nodding over the grass, and there were twelve peach trees that in spring-time broke out into delicate blossoms of pink and pearl, and in the autumn bore rich fruit.

The birds sat on the branches of the trees and sang so very sweetly

that the children used
to stop their games in
order to listen to them.

They felt quite safe because they knew the Giant was not at home, but had gone far away.

"How happy we are here!" they cried to each other.

But one day the Giant came back. He had been all the way to Cornwall to visit his friend the Cornish ogre, and had stayed with him for seven years. After the seven years were over

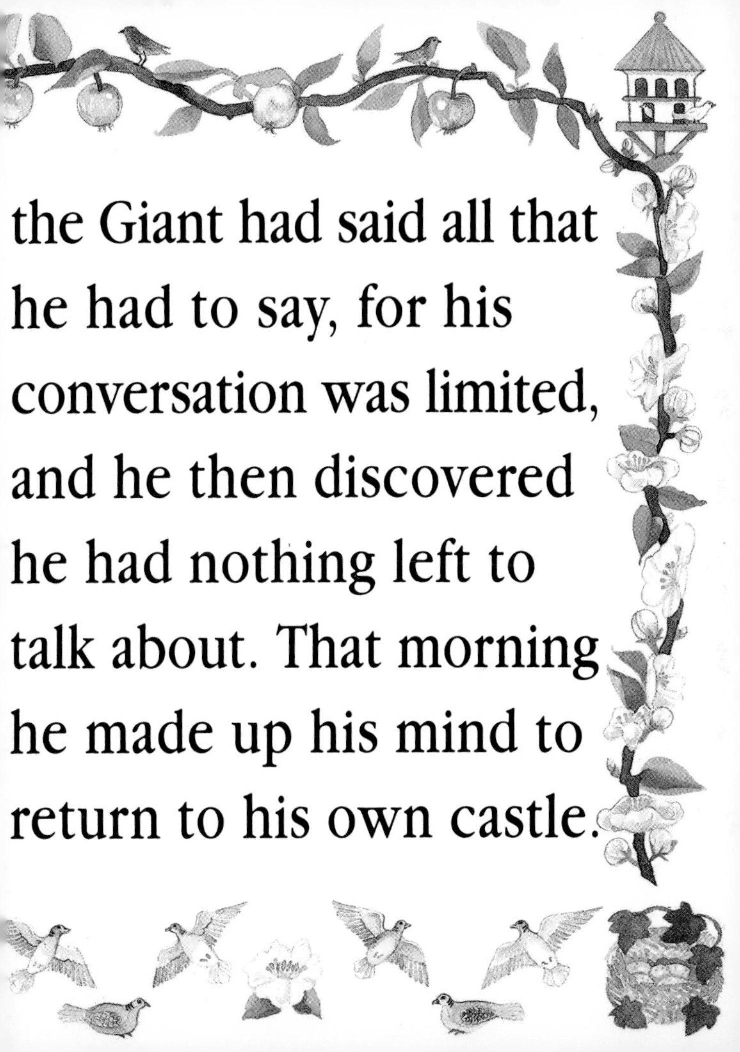

the Giant had said all that he had to say, for his conversation was limited, and he then discovered he had nothing left to talk about. That morning he made up his mind to return to his own castle.

He said goodbye to his friend, the Cornish ogre, and thanked him for a pleasant stay. Then off he set up hill and down dale and before long his giant strides had brought him back to his very own front door.

But the first thing he saw was the children playing in the garden.

"What are you doing here?" he cried in a gruff voice, and the terrified children ran away.

"My own garden is my own garden," said the Giant. "Anyone can understand that, and I will allow nobody to play in it but myself."

So he built a high wall all round it, and put up a sign.

He was a very selfish Giant.

The poor children now had nowhere to play. They tried to play on the road, but the road was very dusty and full of hard stones, and they did not like it. Sadly they remembered the soft grass in the garden.

When their schooldays were over they would wander round the high walls, and talk about the beautiful garden inside.

"How happy we were there!" they sighed, as they scuffed their shoes

along the dusty road.

Then the Spring came and all over the country little birds sang sweetly amongst the blossom. But in the garden of the Selfish Giant it stayed Winter all the time.

TRESPASSERS
WILL BE
PROSECUTED

The birds did not care to sing in the garden for there were no children, and soon the trees forgot to blossom. Once a beautiful flower poked its head out above the grass, but when it saw the Giant's sign it felt so

sorry for the children that it slipped back into the ground again, and went off to sleep. The only people who were pleased with the Selfish Giant were the Snow and the Frost.

"Spring has forgotten this garden," they cried, "so we will live here all the year round." The Snow covered up the grass with her great white cloak, and the Frost painted all the trees silver.

Then they invited the North Wind to stay with them, and gusting and blustering he arrived wrapped all in furs. All day long he roared about the garden until he blew the chimney-pots right off the roof!

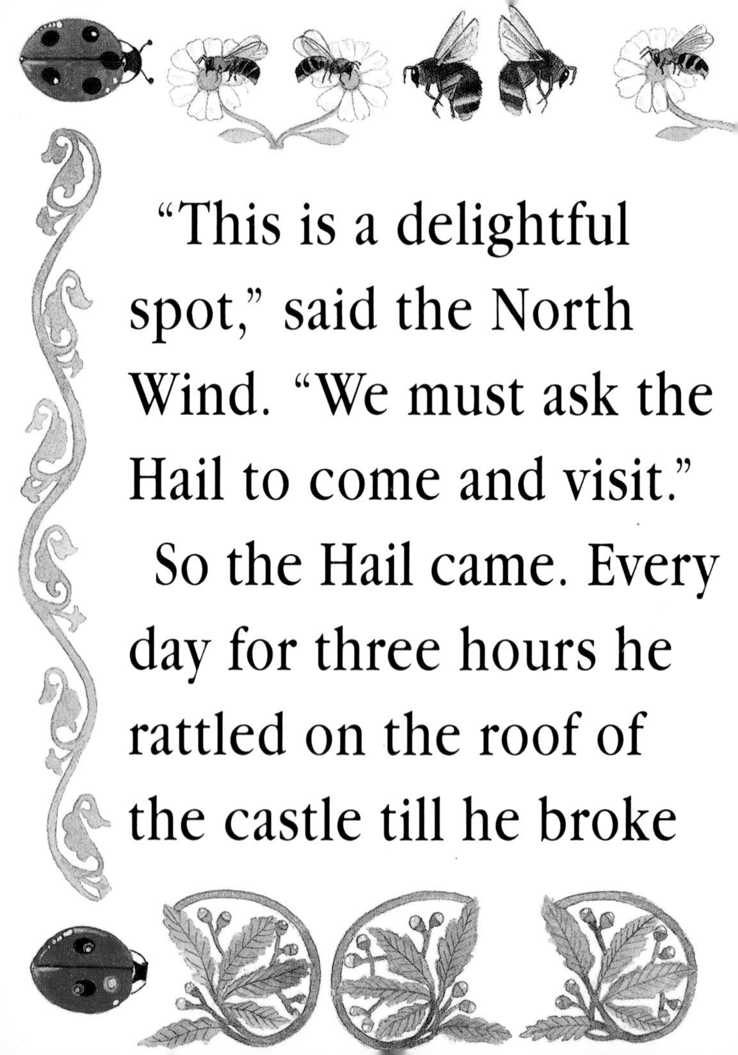

"This is a delightful spot," said the North Wind. "We must ask the Hail to come and visit."

So the Hail came. Every day for three hours he rattled on the roof of the castle till he broke

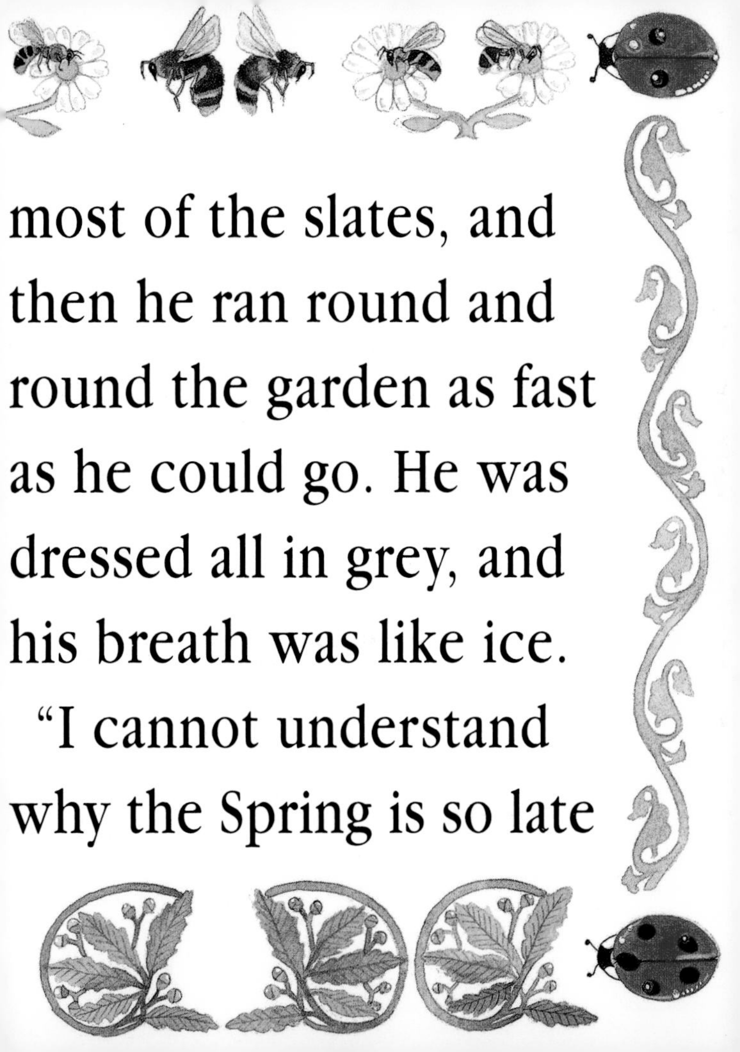

most of the slates, and then he ran round and round the garden as fast as he could go. He was dressed all in grey, and his breath was like ice.

"I cannot understand why the Spring is so late

in coming," said the Selfish Giant, as he sat at the window and looked out at his cold, white garden. "I hope there will be a change in the weather."

But the sweet Spring breezes never came, nor the warm winds of Summer. The Autumn gave golden fruit to every garden, but to the Giant's garden she gave none at all.

"He is too selfish," she

said. So it was always Winter there in the Giant's garden, and the North Wind and the Hail and the Frost and the Snow held hands and danced over the frozen ground and under the bare branches of the trees.

One morning the Giant was lying awake in bed when he heard some lovely music outside his window.

It sounded so sweet to his ears that he thought it must be the King's musicians passing by, but it was only a little linnet singing at the top of his voice! It was so long since the Giant had heard a bird sing in his garden that it seemed to him to be the most beautiful music in the world. And then a strange thing happened. The Hail stopped dancing over the castle roof and the North Wind ceased roaring, and a delicious perfume wafted in through the open window.

“I believe the Spring has come at last,” said the Giant with a slow smile, and he jumped out of bed and looked into his garden.

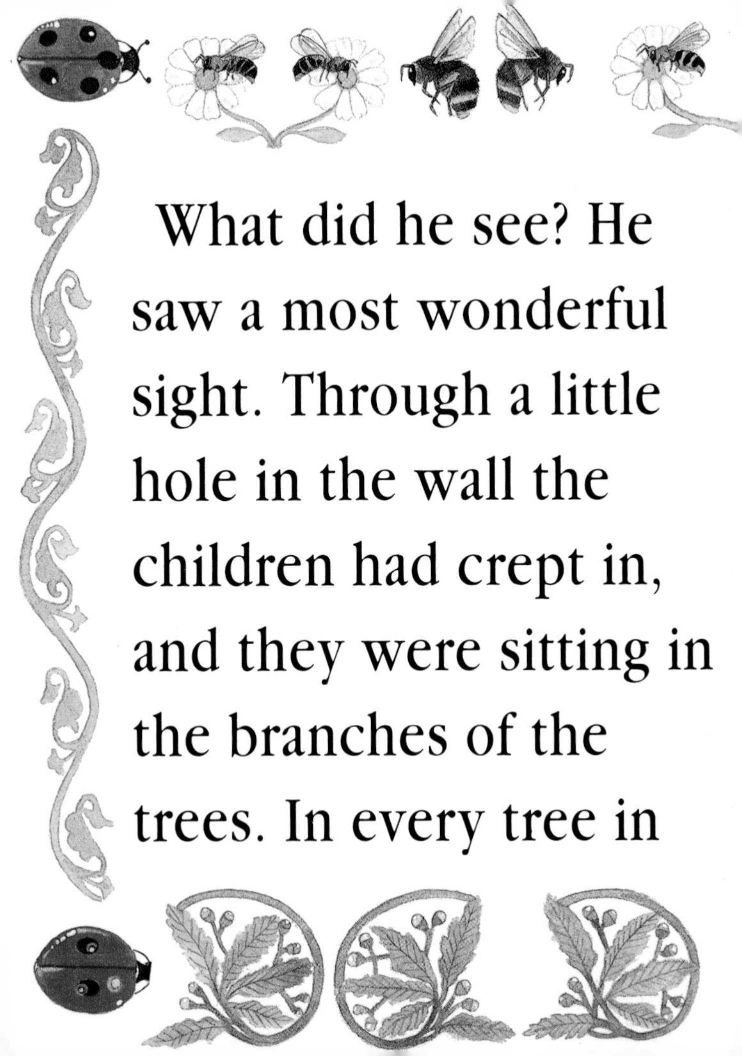

What did he see? He saw a most wonderful sight. Through a little hole in the wall the children had crept in, and they were sitting in the branches of the trees. In every tree in

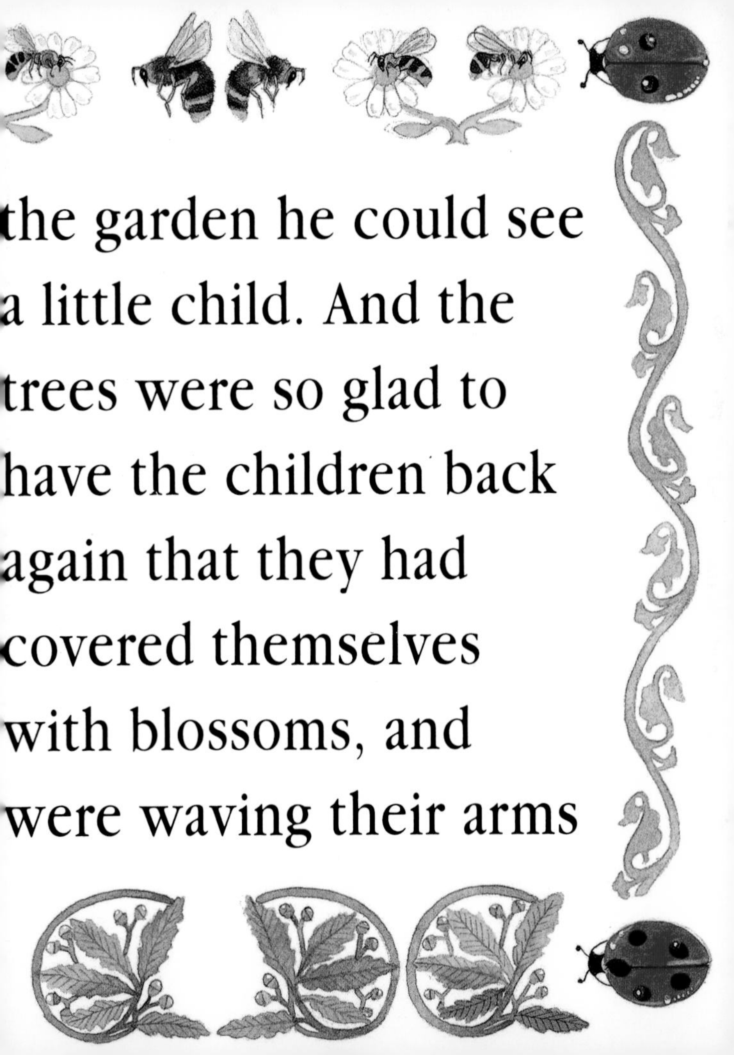

the garden he could see a little child. And the trees were so glad to have the children back again that they had covered themselves with blossoms, and were waving their arms gently high above the children's heads. The birds were flying about and twittering with delight, and the flowers were shyly peeping up through the green grass and laughing. It was indeed a lovely scene.

But in one corner of the garden it was still Winter. It was the farthest corner of all, and there stood a little boy.

He was so small that he could not reach up to the branches of the tree, and sadly he paced all around it, crying bitterly. He longed to climb up as his friends had done but he was

just too short.

The poor tree's bare branches were still covered with frost and snow, and high above it the noisy North Wind blew and roared for all he was worth.

"Climb up, little boy," said the tree, and it bent its branches down as low as it could, but the boy was too tiny.

And the Giant's heart melted as he looked out and saw the unhappy child. "How selfish I have been!" he said. "Now I know why the Spring would not come here. I will put that

poor little boy on the top of the tree, and then I will knock down the wall, and my garden shall be the children's playground for ever." He was really very sorry for what he had done.

So he crept downstairs and opened the front door quite softly, and went out into the garden.

But when the children saw him coming they were so frightened that they scrambled down from the trees and ran away, and then the garden became like Winter again.

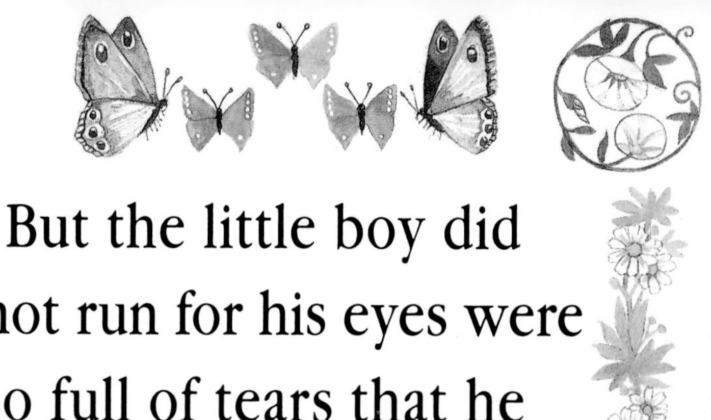

But the little boy did not run for his eyes were so full of tears that he could not see the Giant coming. And so the Giant took him gently in his hand, and lifted him up into the tree.

And the tree broke at once into blossom, and the birds came and sang on it, and the little boy stretched out his two arms and flung them round the Giant's neck, and kissed him on his rough cheek.

And when the other children saw that the Giant was no longer wicked, they came running back, and with them came the Spring.

"It is your garden now, little children," said the Giant and he took a great axe and knocked down the wall.

And when the people of the village returned with brimming baskets from market at twelve o'clock they found the Giant playing with the children in the most beautiful garden they had ever seen.

All day long they played, and in the evening they came to the Giant to bid him goodbye.

"But where is your little companion?" he said. "Where is the boy I put into the tree?" The Giant loved him the best because the little boy had kissed him and the poor Giant had never

been kissed before.

"We don't know," answered the children. "He has gone away."

"You must tell him to be sure and come tomorrow," said the Giant. But the children said that they did not know where he lived and had never seen him before, and then the Giant felt very sad.

Every afternoon when school had ended, the children came and played with the Giant.

But the little boy
whom the Giant loved
was never seen again.
The Giant was very
kind to all the children,
yet he longed for his
first little friend and
often wondered what
had become of him.

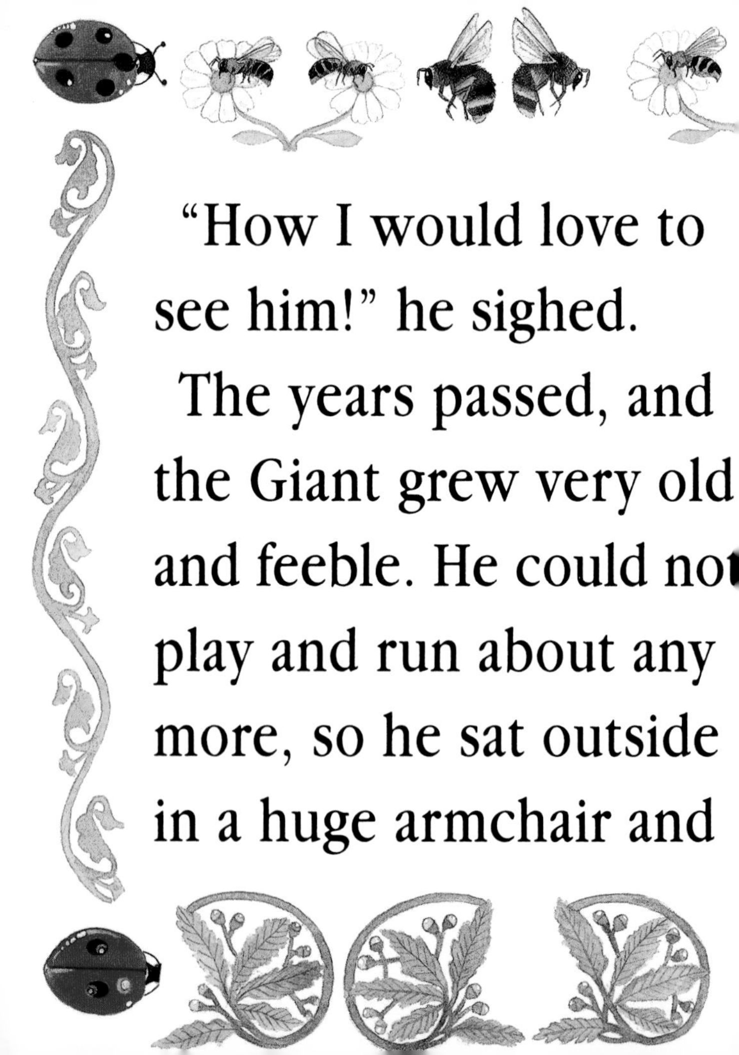

"How I would love to see him!" he sighed.

The years passed, and the Giant grew very old and feeble. He could not play and run about any more, so he sat outside in a huge armchair and

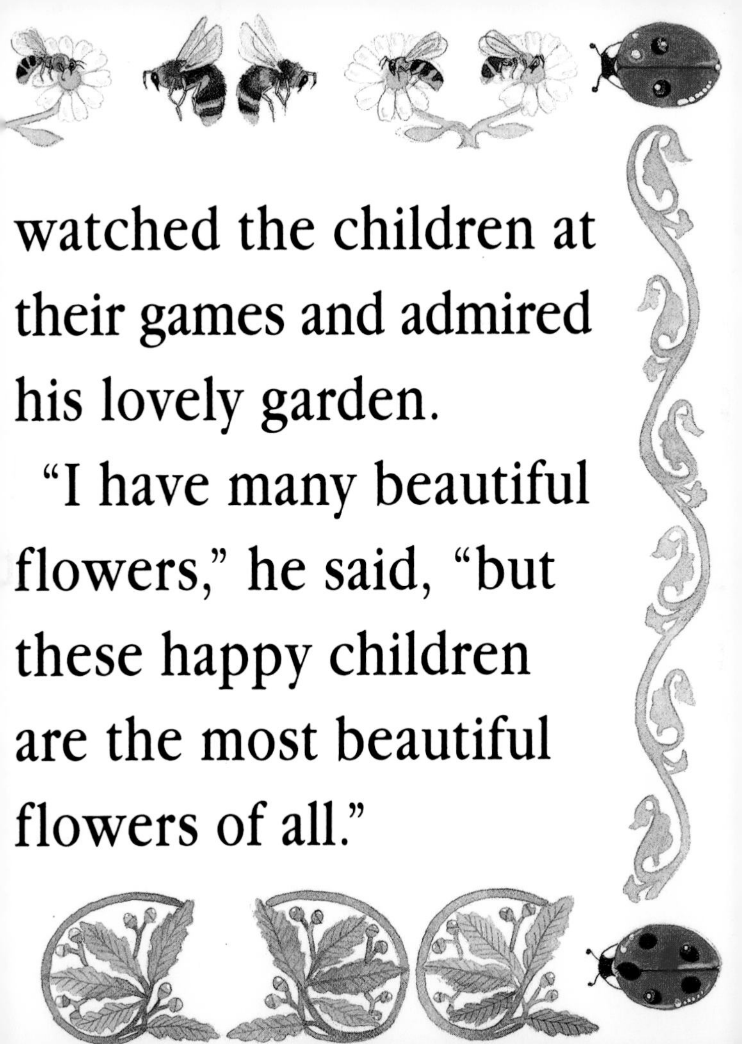

watched the children at their games and admired his lovely garden.

"I have many beautiful flowers," he said, "but these happy children are the most beautiful flowers of all."

One Winter morning he looked out of his bedroom window as he was dressing. He did not hate the Winter now, for he knew that it was merely the Spring asleep, and that the flowers were

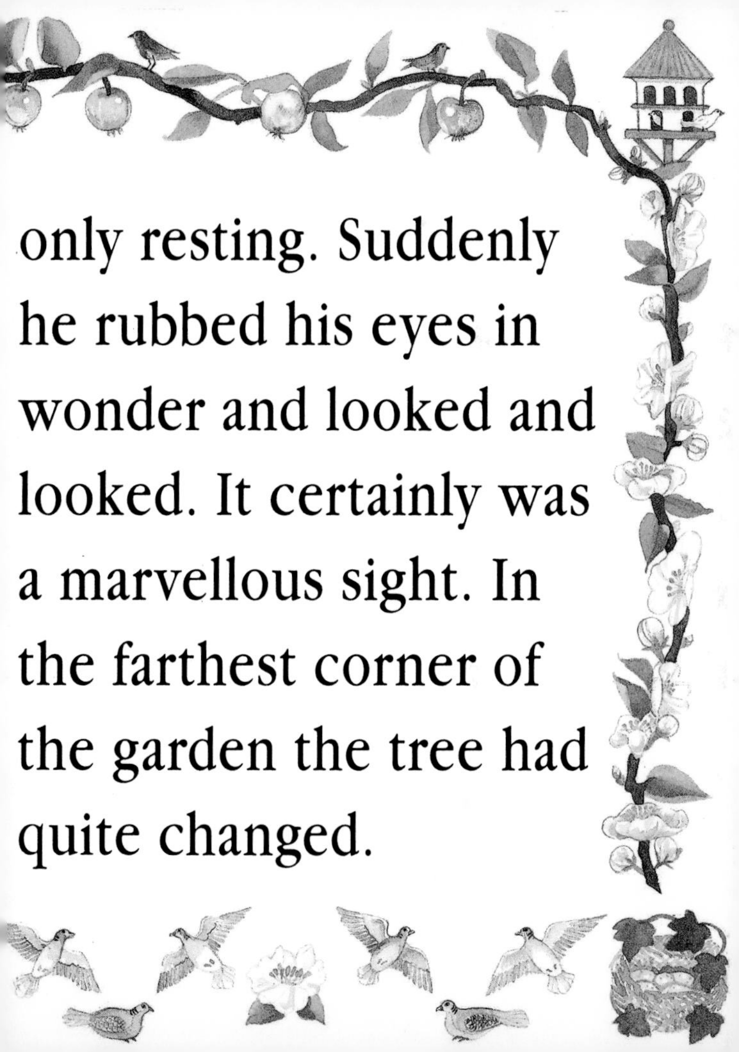

only resting. Suddenly he rubbed his eyes in wonder and looked and looked. It certainly was a marvellous sight. In the farthest corner of the garden the tree had quite changed.

Lovely white blossoms covered its golden branches and silver fruit hung down from every bough.

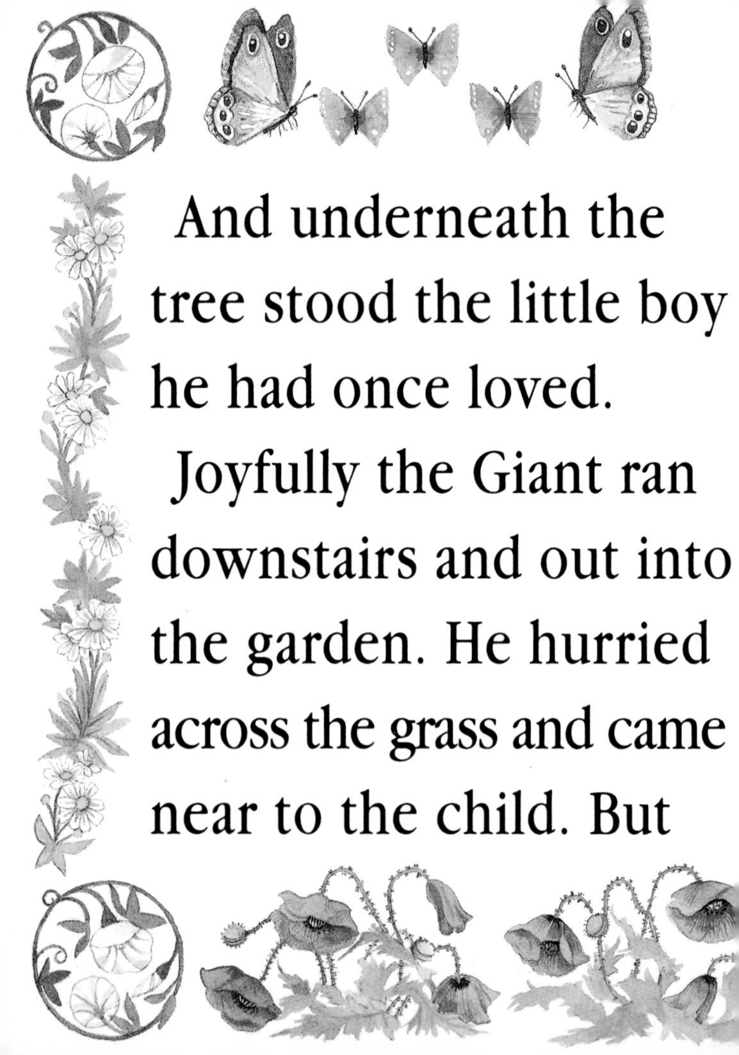

And underneath the tree stood the little boy he had once loved.

Joyfully the Giant ran downstairs and out into the garden. He hurried across the grass and came near to the child. But

when he grew quite close the Giant's face grew red with anger as he looked at the little boy.

"Who has dared to wound thee?" he cried, for on the palms of the child's hands were the

prints of two nails, and
the prints of two nails
were on his little feet.

"Who has dared to wound thee?" asked the Giant once again. "Tell me, so that I may take my big sword and slay him at once."

"No," answered the child with a gentle smile.

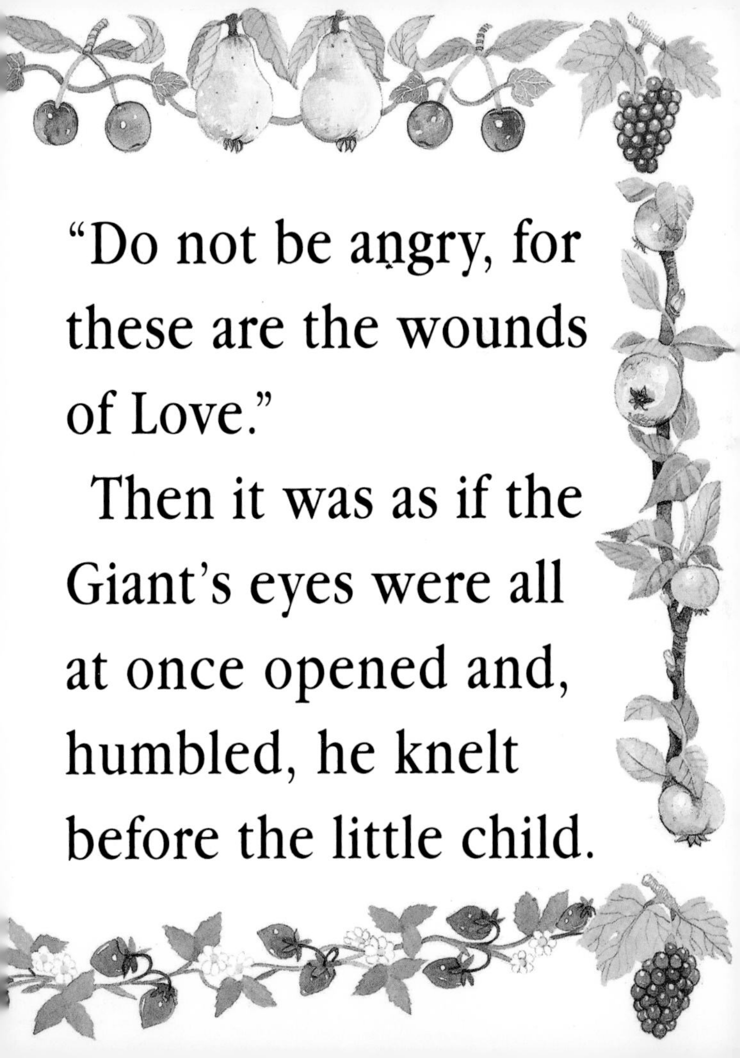

"Do not be angry, for these are the wounds of Love."

Then it was as if the Giant's eyes were all at once opened and, humbled, he knelt before the little child.

"Who art thou?" he said. And the child smiled at the Giant, and said to him gently,

"You let me play once in your garden. Today you shall come with me to my garden, which is Paradise."

And when the children ran in to play that afternoon, they found the Giant lying dead under the tree, all covered with white blossoms.

But from then on Spring always came early to the Giant's garden and in time the children's children played there just as they had done.

The
Happy Prince

High above the city on a tall column stood the statue of the Happy Prince. He was gilded all over with thin leaves of fine gold, for eyes he had two bright sapphires and a large red ruby glowed on his sword-hilt.

The city people were very proud of their fine statue.

"Why can't you be like the Happy Prince?" asked a sensible mother when she found her little boy crying for the moon. "The Happy Prince never dreams of crying for anything."

"I am glad to see there is someone in the world who is quite happy," muttered a disappointed man as he gazed at the wonderful statue.

"He looks just like an angel," said the Charity Children as they came out of the cathedral in their bright scarlet cloaks and

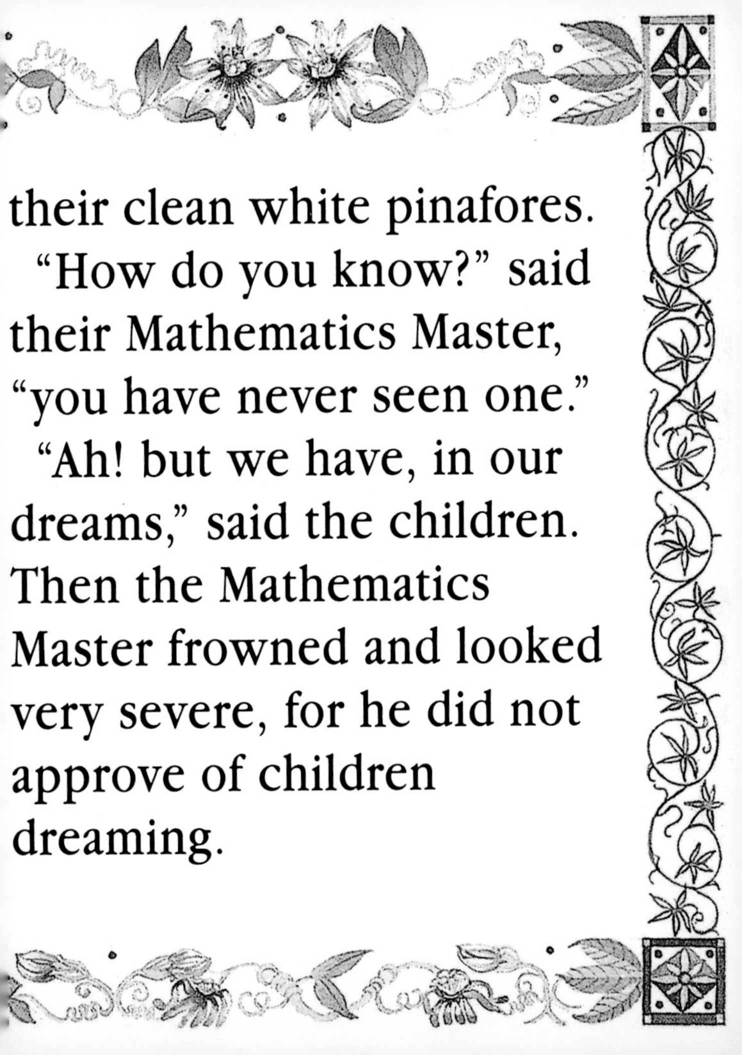

their clean white pinafores.
"How do you know?" said their Mathematics Master, "you have never seen one."
"Ah! but we have, in our dreams," said the children. Then the Mathematics Master frowned and looked very severe, for he did not approve of children dreaming.

Far away from the city lived a little Swallow. His friends had gone away to Egypt six weeks before, but he had stayed behind, for he was in love with the most beautiful Reed.

He had met her early in the spring as he was flying down the river after a big yellow moth, and he had been so attracted by her slender waist that he had stopped to talk to her.

"Shall I love you?" said the Swallow, who liked to come to the point at once, and the Reed made him a low bow in reply. So he flew happily round and round her, touching the water with his wings, and making silver ripples. This was his courtship, and it lasted all through the summer.

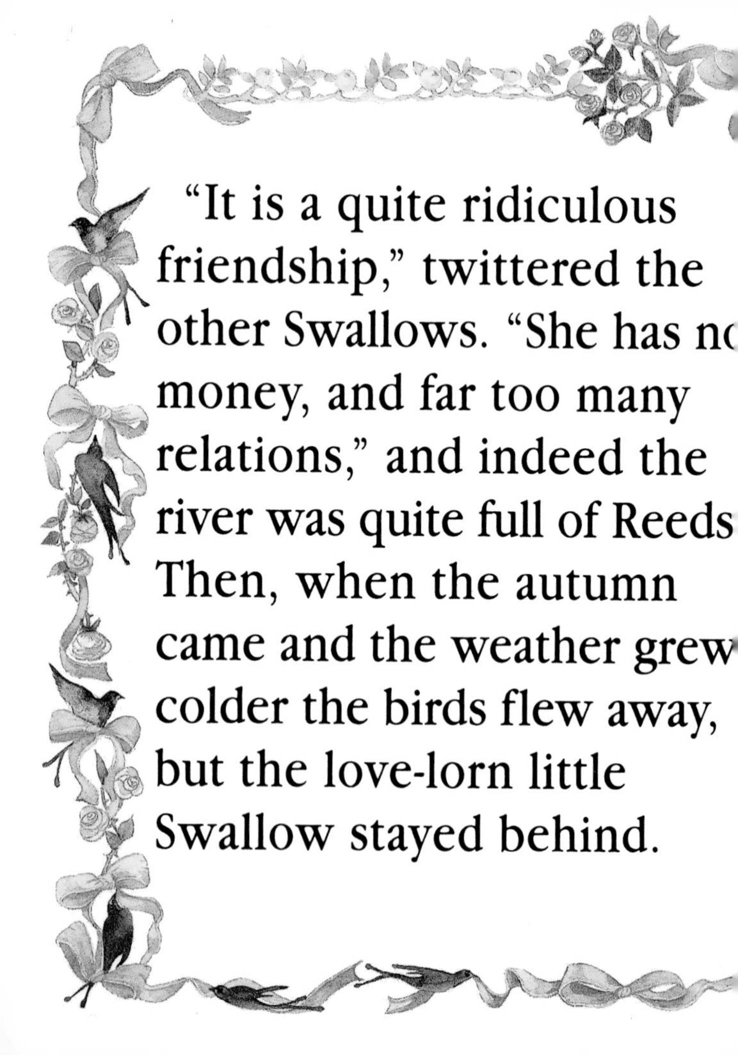

"It is a quite ridiculous friendship," twittered the other Swallows. "She has no money, and far too many relations," and indeed the river was quite full of Reeds. Then, when the autumn came and the weather grew colder the birds flew away, but the love-lorn little Swallow stayed behind.

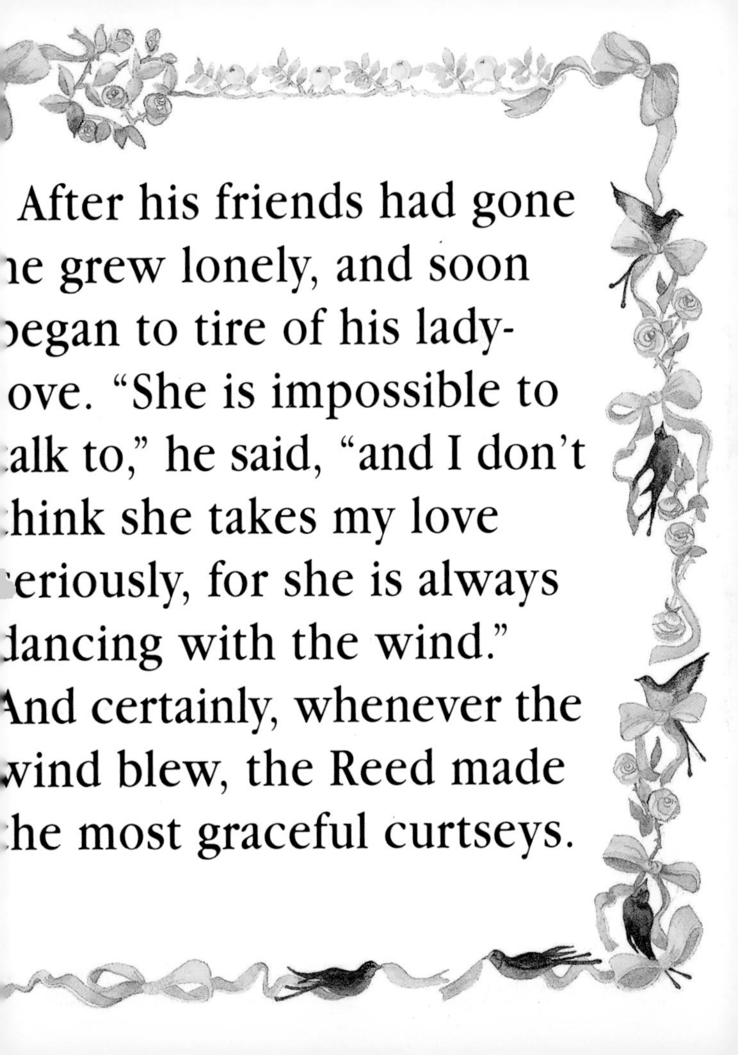

After his friends had gone he grew lonely, and soon began to tire of his lady-love. "She is impossible to talk to," he said, "and I don't think she takes my love seriously, for she is always dancing with the wind." And certainly, whenever the wind blew, the Reed made the most graceful curtseys.

"Will you come away with me?" he said to her finally, but the Reed shook her head. She was too fond of her home.

"You have been trifling with me," he cried. "I am off to the Pyramids in Egypt. Good-bye!" and away he flew.

All day long he flew, and

at night-time he arrived at the city. “Where shall I stay?” he wondered.

Then he saw the statue on the tall column.

“There is a fine position, with plenty of fresh air.” So he alighted right between the feet of the Happy Prince.

“I have a golden bedroom,” he said softly to himself as

he prepared to go to sleep, but just as he put his head under his wing a large drop of water fell on him.

"What a curious thing!" he cried. "There is not a single cloud in the sky, the stars are quite clear and bright, and yet it is raining. The climate in the north of Europe is really dreadful."

Then another drop fell.
"What is the use of a statue if it cannot keep the rain off?" he said. "I must look for a good chimney-pot," and he got ready to fly away.

But before he had opened his wings, a third drop fell. He looked up and saw — ah! what did he see?

The eyes of the Happy Prince were filled with tears, and tears were running down his golden cheeks. His face was so beautiful in the moonlight that the little Swallow was filled with pity.

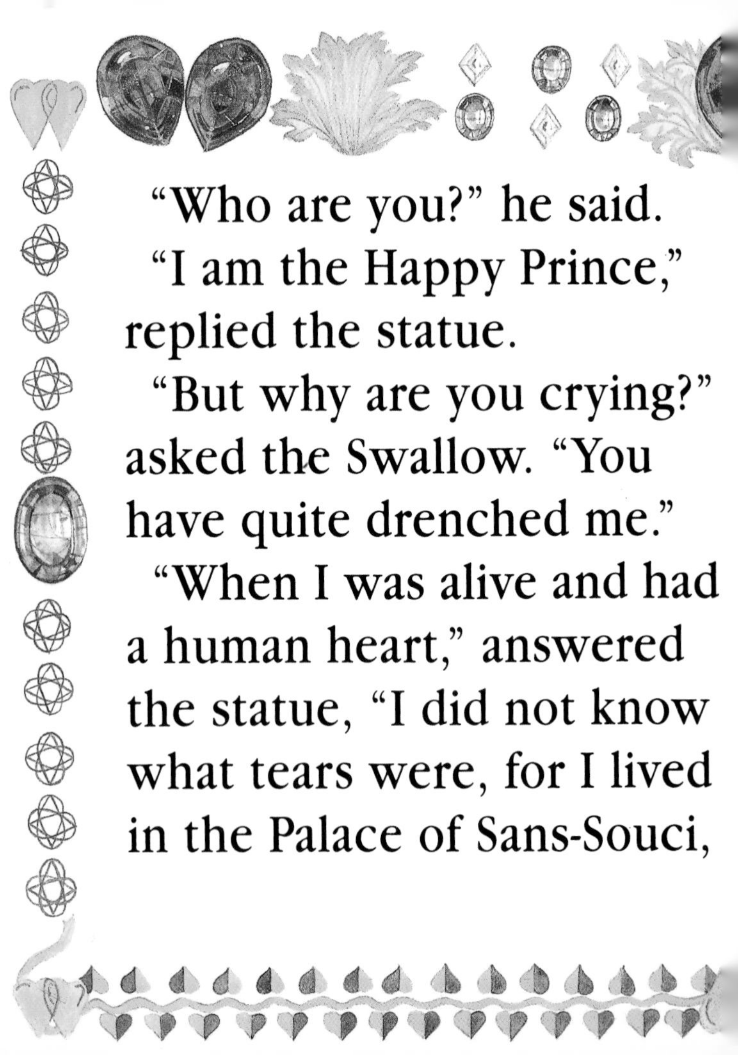

"Who are you?" he said.
"I am the Happy Prince," replied the statue.

"But why are you crying?" asked the Swallow. "You have quite drenched me."

"When I was alive and had a human heart," answered the statue, "I did not know what tears were, for I lived in the Palace of Sans-Souci,

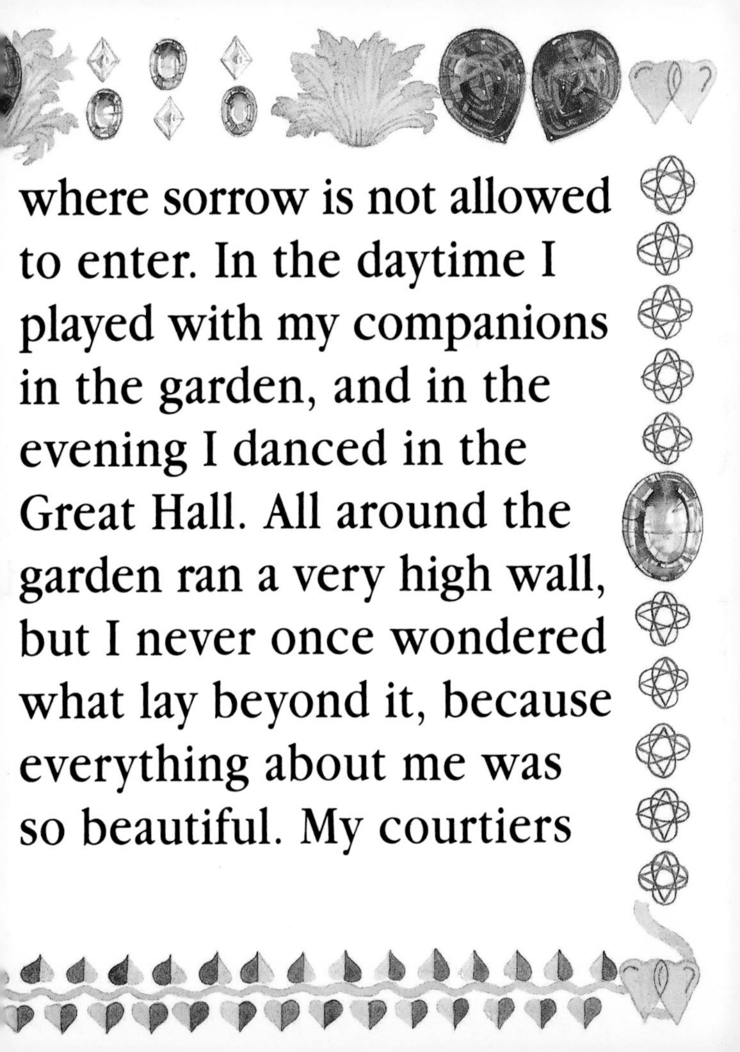

where sorrow is not allowed to enter. In the daytime I played with my companions in the garden, and in the evening I danced in the Great Hall. All around the garden ran a very high wall, but I never once wondered what lay beyond it, because everything about me was so beautiful. My courtiers

called me the Happy Prince, and happy indeed I was, if pleasure be happiness. So I lived, and so I died. And now that I am dead they have set me up here so high that I can see all the ugliness and all the misery of my city, and though my heart is made of lead yet I cannot help but weep.

"Far away in a little street there is a poor house," continued the statue in a low musical voice. "One of the windows is open, and through it I can see a woman seated at a table."

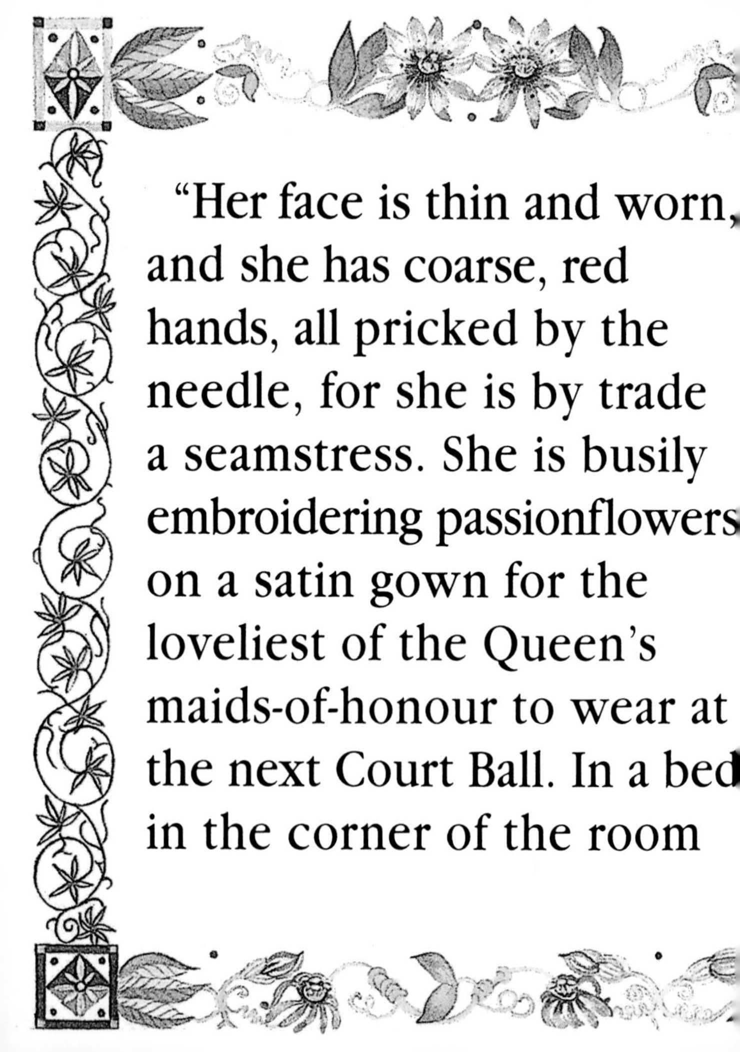

"Her face is thin and worn, and she has coarse, red hands, all pricked by the needle, for she is by trade a seamstress. She is busily embroidering passionflowers on a satin gown for the loveliest of the Queen's maids-of-honour to wear at the next Court Ball. In a bed in the corner of the room her little boy is lying ill. He has a fever, and is asking for oranges. His mother has nothing to give him but river water, so he is crying. Swallow, Swallow, little Swallow, will you not take her the ruby out of my sword-hilt? My feet are fastened to this pedestal and I cannot move."

“My friends are waiting for me in Egypt,” said the little Swallow. “They are flying up and down the River Nile over the large lotus-flowers. Soon they will go to sleep

in the tomb of the great King. There he lies in his painted coffin. He is wrapped in soft yellow linen, and embalmed with spices. Round his neck is a chain

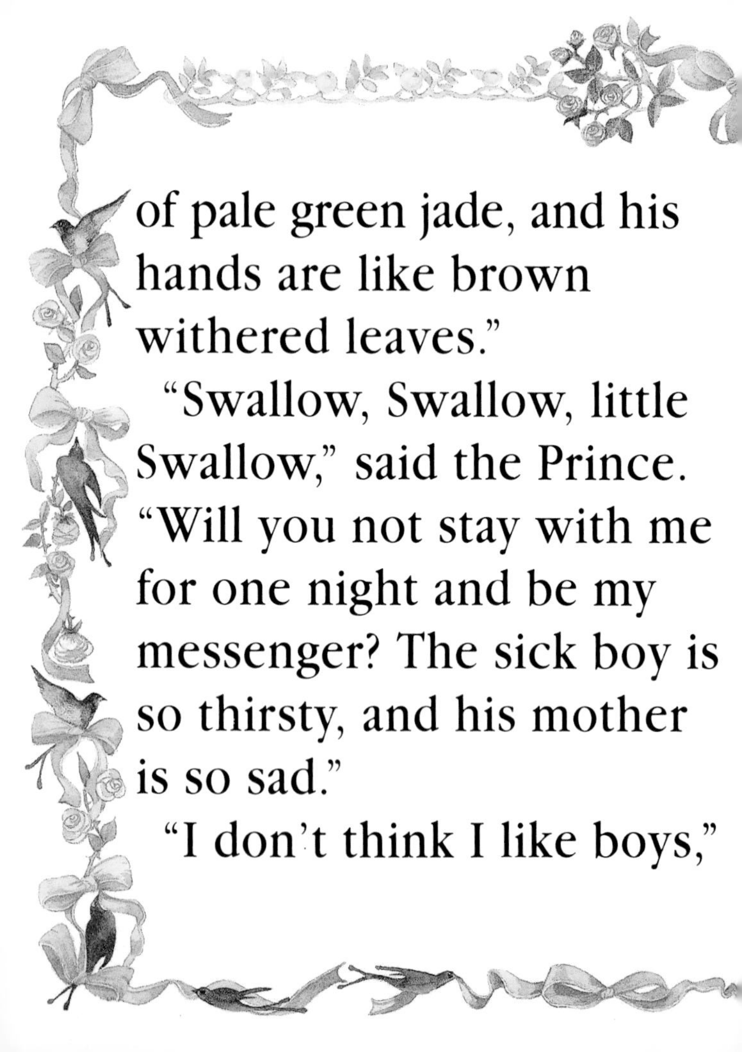

of pale green jade, and his hands are like brown withered leaves."

"Swallow, Swallow, little Swallow," said the Prince. "Will you not stay with me for one night and be my messenger? The sick boy is so thirsty, and his mother is so sad."

"I don't think I like boys,"

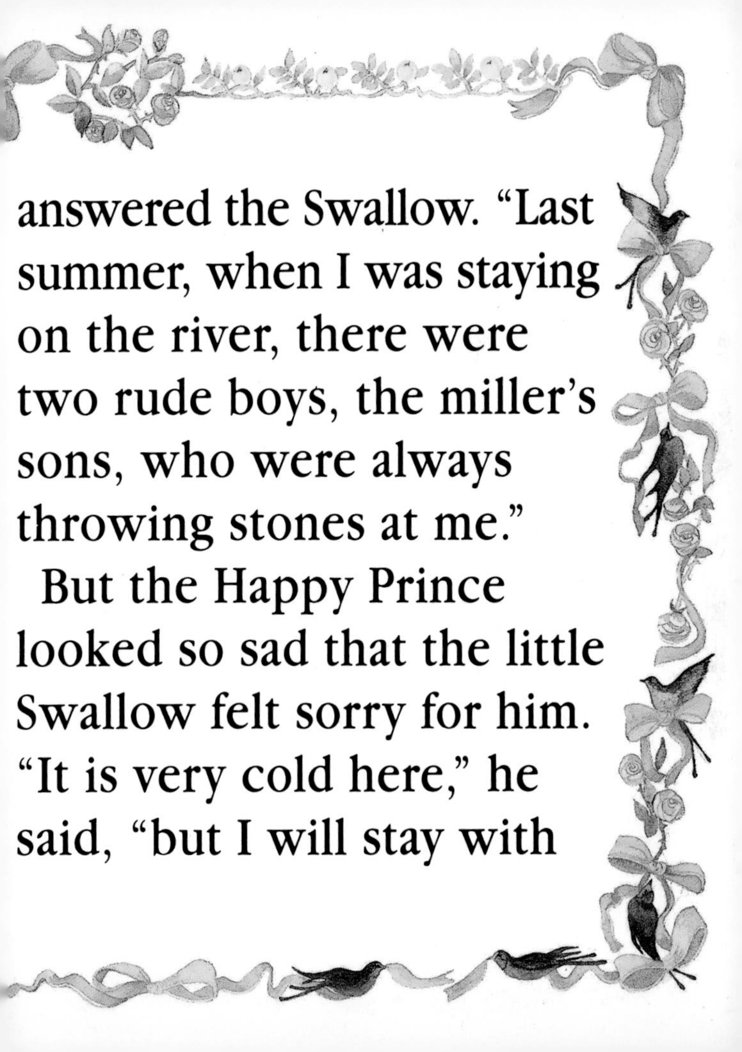

answered the Swallow. “Last summer, when I was staying on the river, there were two rude boys, the miller’s sons, who were always throwing stones at me.”

But the Happy Prince looked so sad that the little Swallow felt sorry for him. “It is very cold here,” he said, “but I will stay with you for one night, and be your messenger."

"Thank you, little Swallow," said the Prince.

So the Swallow picked out the great ruby from the Prince's sword, and flew away with it in his beak over the roofs of the town. He passed by the cathedral's white marble angels.

He passed by the Palace and heard the sound of dancing. A beautiful girl came out on the balcony with her lover.

"How wonderful the stars are tonight," he said to her, "and how wonderful is the power of love!"

"I hope my dress will be ready in time for the State Ball," she answered. "I have ordered passionflowers to be embroidered on it, but the seamstresses are so lazy."

He passed over the river, and at last he came to the poor house and looked in at the window. The boy tossed feverishly on his bed.

His mother was so tired that she had fallen asleep. The little Swallow hopped through the window and laid the great ruby on the table beside the woman's thimble. Then he flew round the bed, gently fanning the boy's forehead with his wings.

"How cool I feel!" said

the boy. "I must be getting better," and he sank into a delicious slumber.

Then the Swallow flew back to the Happy Prince, and told him what he had done. "It is curious," the little bird remarked, "but I feel quite warm now, even though the night is so bitterly cold."

"That is because you have done a good deed," said the Happy Prince. Then the little Swallow began to think, but soon he fell fast asleep. Thinking always made him sleepy.

When day broke he flew down to the river and had a bath. "What a remarkable phenomenon!" said the

Professor of Ornithology (which, as I am sure you already know, is the study of birds) as he was passing over the bridge. "A swallow in winter!"

"To-night I fly to Egypt," said the Swallow happily. He flew all over the city and wherever he went the Sparrows chirruped, and said to each other, "Look! There is a swallow. What a distinguished stranger!" so he enjoyed himself greatly.

When the moon rose he flew to the Happy Prince.

"Is there anything you want me to bring back from Egypt?" he cried. "I am just leaving."

"Swallow, Swallow, little Swallow," said the Prince. "Will you not stay with me one night longer?"

"They are waiting for me in Egypt," answered the Swallow. "Tomorrow my friends will fly up the River Nile to the great waterfall. At noon the yellow lions come down to the water's edge to drink. They have eyes like green beryl jewels, and their roar is louder than the roar of the waterfall."

"Swallow, Swallow, little Swallow," said the Prince. "Far away across the city I see a young man in a cramped attic. He is leaning over a desk covered with papers, and in a glass by his side there is a bunch of withered violets. His hair is brown and shiny and his lips are red as a pomegranate."

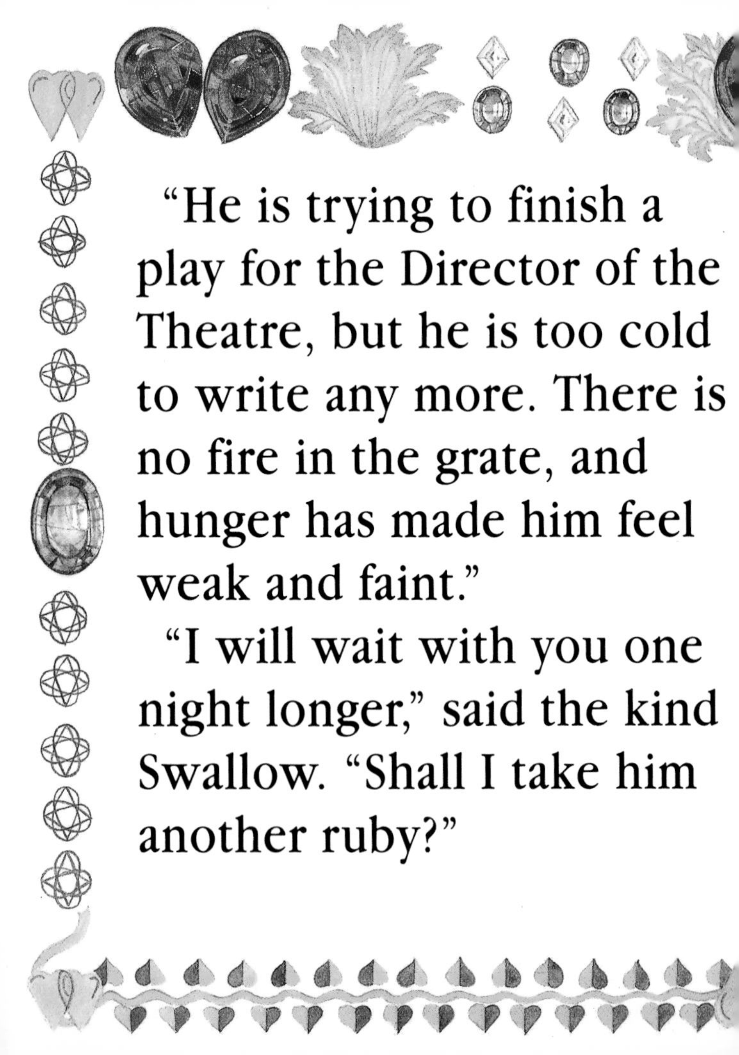

"He is trying to finish a play for the Director of the Theatre, but he is too cold to write any more. There is no fire in the grate, and hunger has made him feel weak and faint."

"I will wait with you one night longer," said the kind Swallow. "Shall I take him another ruby?"

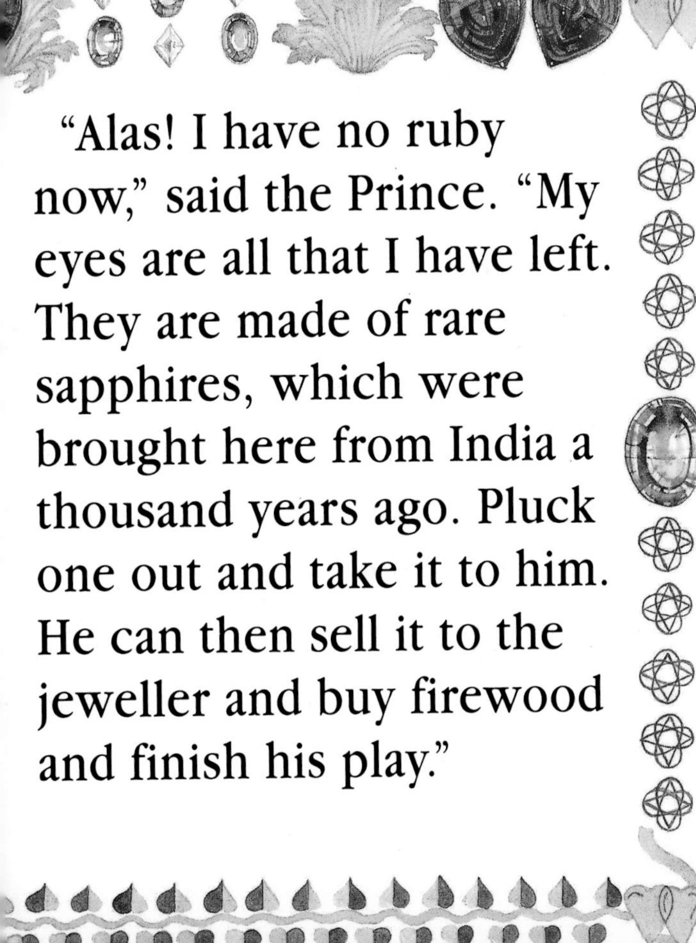

"Alas! I have no ruby now," said the Prince. "My eyes are all that I have left. They are made of rare sapphires, which were brought here from India a thousand years ago. Pluck one out and take it to him. He can then sell it to the jeweller and buy firewood and finish his play."

"Dear Prince," said the Swallow. "I cannot do that," and he began to weep.

"Swallow, Swallow, little Swallow," said the Prince. "Do as I command you."

So the Swallow plucked out the Prince's eye, and flew away to the student's attic. It was easy enough to get in, as there was a hole in the roof.

There was the young man with his head buried in his hands. He did not hear the flutter of the bird's wings, but later when he looked up he found the beautiful blue sapphire lying on top of the withered violets.

"Appreciation at last," he cried gladly.

"This must be from some great admirer. Someone believes in me after all and now I can finish my play," and the young man happily rubbed his hands.

The next day the Swallow flew down to the harbour. He watched the sailors hauling big chests out of the hold with strong ropes. "Heave a-hoy!" they called as each chest came up.

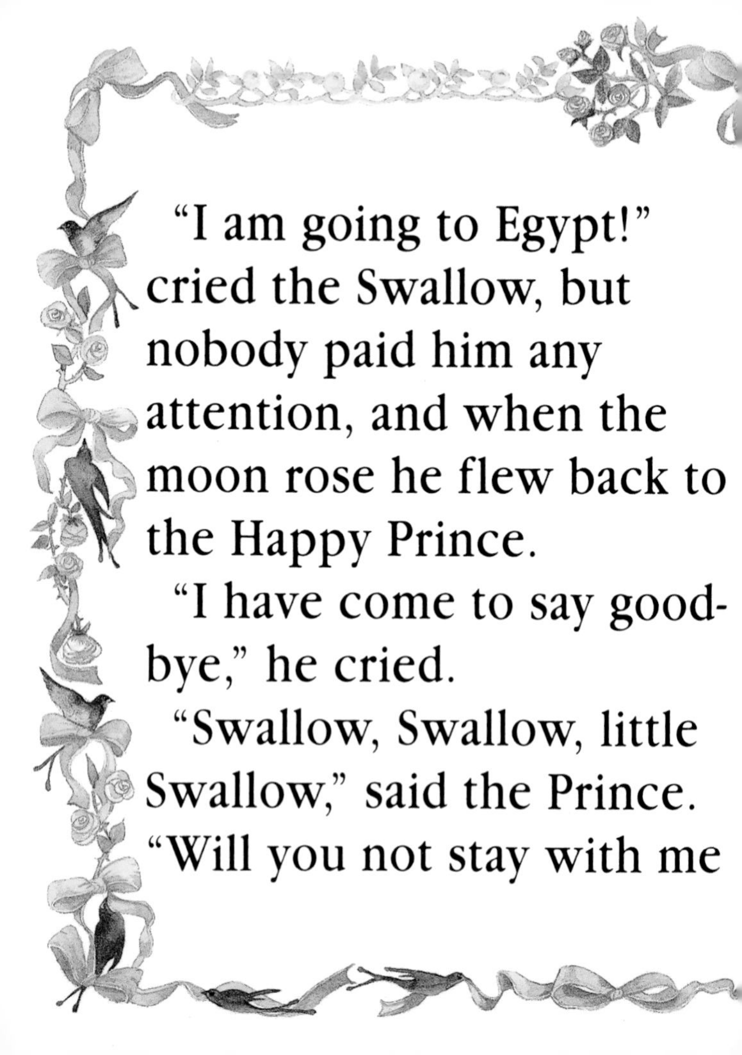

"I am going to Egypt!" cried the Swallow, but nobody paid him any attention, and when the moon rose he flew back to the Happy Prince.

"I have come to say good-bye," he cried.

"Swallow, Swallow, little Swallow," said the Prince. "Will you not stay with me

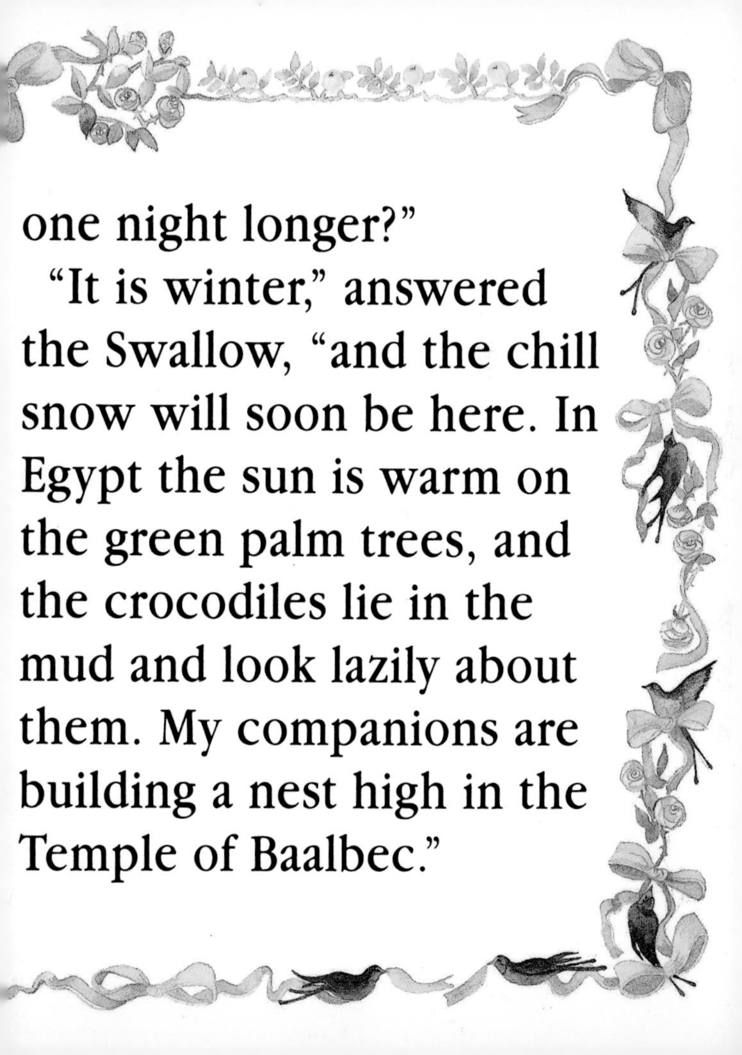

one night longer?"

"It is winter," answered the Swallow, "and the chill snow will soon be here. In Egypt the sun is warm on the green palm trees, and the crocodiles lie in the mud and look lazily about them. My companions are building a nest high in the Temple of Baalbec."

"There the pink and white doves are watching them, and cooing to each other. Dear Prince, I must leave you, but I will never forget you, and next spring I will bring you two beautiful jewels. The ruby shall be redder than a red rose, and the sapphire shall be as blue as the great sea."

"In the square below," said the Happy Prince, "there stands a little match-girl. She has let her matches fall in the gutter, and they are all spoiled. Her father will beat her if she does not bring home some money, and she is crying. She has no shoes or stockings, and her little head is bare. Pluck out my other eye, and give it to her, and her father will not beat her."

"I will stay with you one night longer," said the Swallow, "but I cannot pluck out your eye. You would be quite blind then."

"Swallow, Swallow, little Swallow," said the Prince. "Do as I command you."

So he plucked out the Prince's other eye, and flew down through the air. He swooped past the match-girl, and slipped the jewel into the palm of her hand.

"What a lovely bit of glass!" cried the little girl and she ran home, laughing.

Then the Swallow slowly flew back to the Prince.

"You are blind now," he said, "so I will stay with you always."

"No, little Swallow," said the poor Prince. "You must go away to Egypt."

"I will stay with you always," said the Swallow, and he slept at the Prince's golden feet.

All the next day he sat on

the Prince's shoulder, and told him stories of what he had seen in strange lands. He told him of the red birds, who stand in long rows on the banks of the Nile and catch goldfish in their beaks. He told him of the Sphinx, who is as old as the world itself and lives in the desert and knows

everything. He told him of the merchants, who walk slowly by the side of their camels and carry amber beads in their hands. He told him of the King of the Mountains of the Moon, who is as black as ebony and worships a large crystal. He told him of the great green snake that sleeps in a palm tree and has twenty priests to feed it with honey-cakes; and of the pygmies who sail over a big lake on large flat leaves, and are always at war with the butterflies.

"Dear little Swallow," said the Prince, "you tell me of marvellous things, but what of the suffering of people?

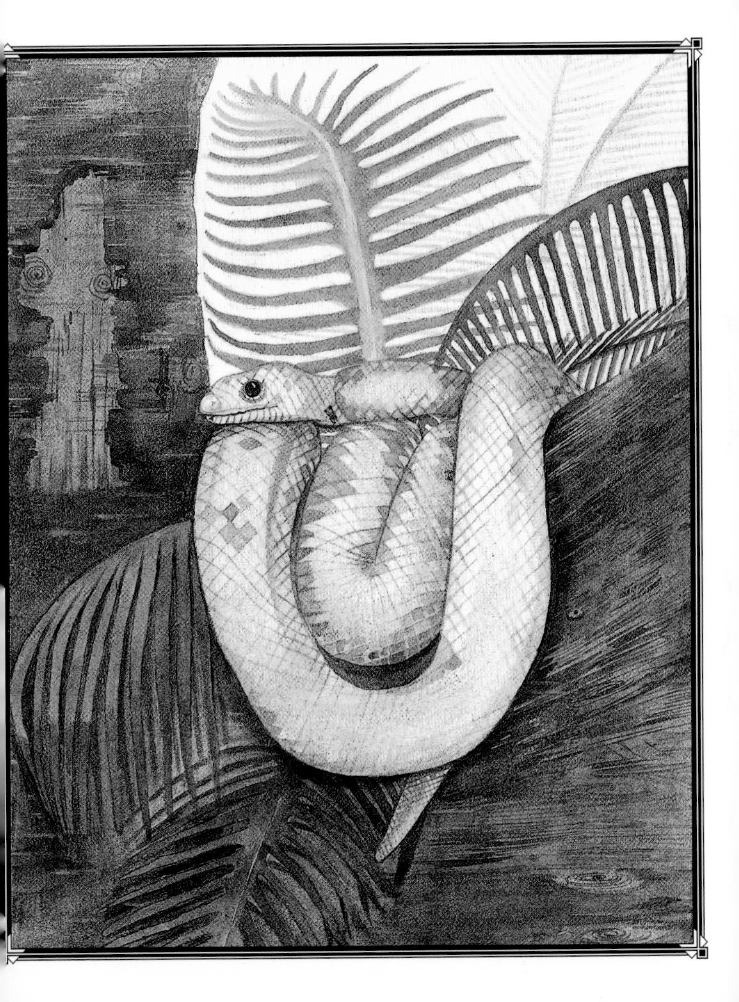

There is no Mystery so great as Misery. Fly over my city, little Swallow, and tell me what you see there."

So the Swallow flew over the great city, and saw the rich making merry in their beautiful houses, while the beggars were sitting at the gates. He flew into dark lanes, and saw the white

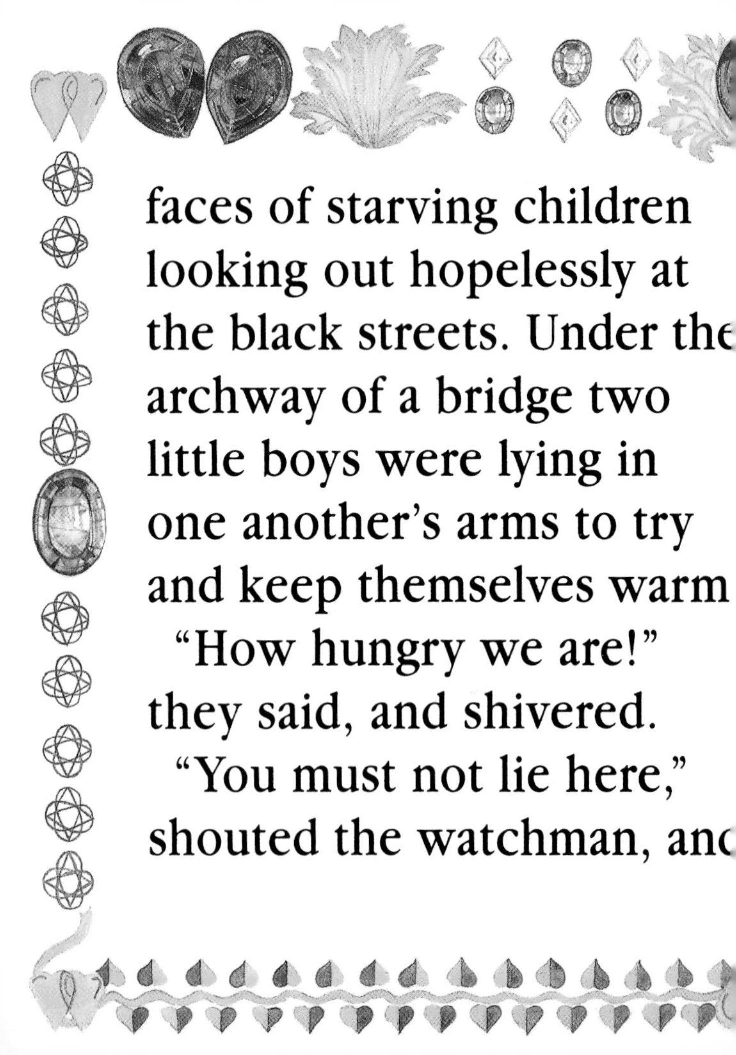

faces of starving children looking out hopelessly at the black streets. Under the archway of a bridge two little boys were lying in one another's arms to try and keep themselves warm

"How hungry we are!" they said, and shivered.

"You must not lie here," shouted the watchman, and

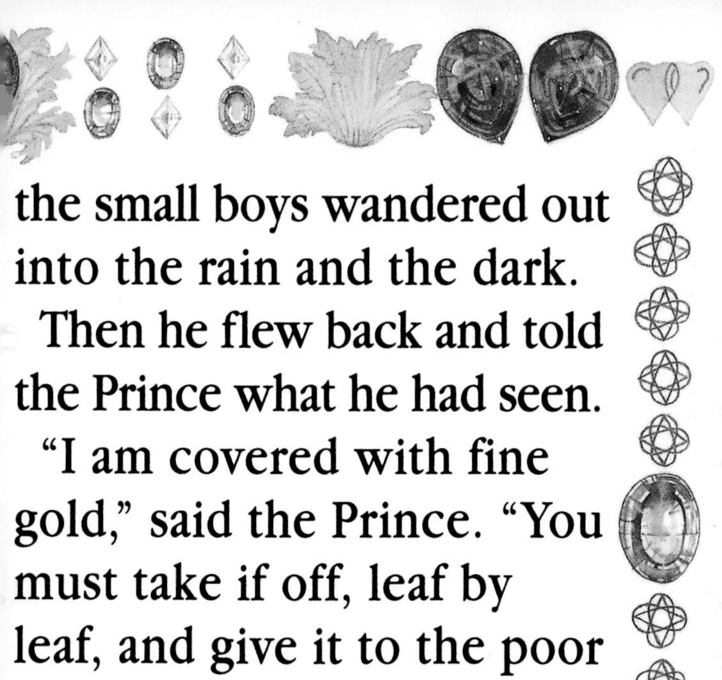

the small boys wandered out into the rain and the dark.

Then he flew back and told the Prince what he had seen.

"I am covered with fine gold," said the Prince. "You must take if off, leaf by leaf, and give it to the poor of my city. People always think that gold can make them happy."

So the Swallow picked off leaf after leaf of the fine gold, till the Happy Prince looked quite dull and grey. Leaf after leaf of the fine gold he brought to the poor, and the children's faces grew rosier, and they laughed and played games in the street. "We have bread now!" they cried.

Then the snow came, and after the snow came the frost. The streets looked as if they were made of silver, and long icicles like crystal daggers hung down from the eaves of the houses.

Everybody went about in furs but the poor little Swallow grew colder and colder. Now he would not leave the Prince for he loved him too well. He picked up crumbs outside the baker's door when the baker was not looking, and tried to keep himself warm by flapping his wings.

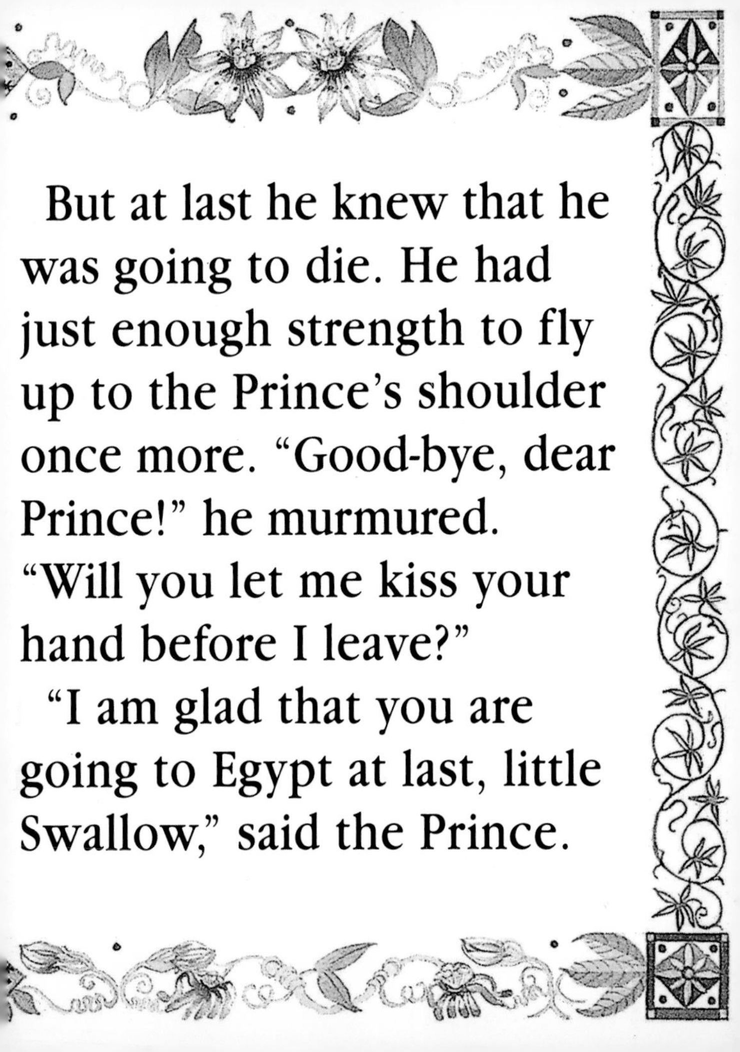

But at last he knew that he was going to die. He had just enough strength to fly up to the Prince's shoulder once more. "Good-bye, dear Prince!" he murmured. "Will you let me kiss your hand before I leave?"

"I am glad that you are going to Egypt at last, little Swallow," said the Prince.

"You have stayed too long here, but you must kiss me on the lips, for I love you."

"It is not to Egypt that I am going," said the Swallow. "I am going to the House of Death. Death is the brother of Sleep, is he not?"

And he kissed the Happy Prince on the lips, and fell down dead at his feet.

At that moment a curious crack sounded inside the statue, as if something had broken. The fact is that the leaden heart had snapped right in two. It certainly was a dreadfully hard frost.

Early the next morning the Mayor and the Town Councillors were walking in the square below.

E
W

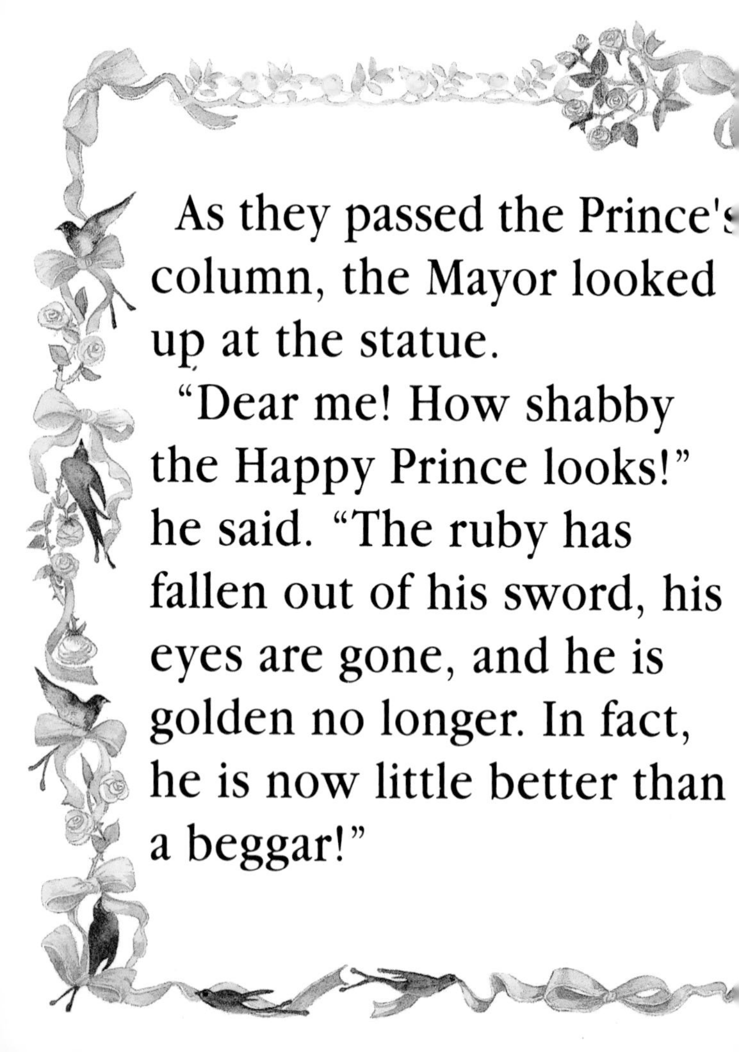

As they passed the Prince's column, the Mayor looked up at the statue.

"Dear me! How shabby the Happy Prince looks!" he said. "The ruby has fallen out of his sword, his eyes are gone, and he is golden no longer. In fact, he is now little better than a beggar!"

"Little better than a beggar," agreed all the Councillors.

"And here is a dead bird at his feet!" continued the Mayor. "We must issue a ruling that birds are not allowed to die here."

So they pulled down the statue of the Happy Prince and carried him off to the furnace to be melted. Then

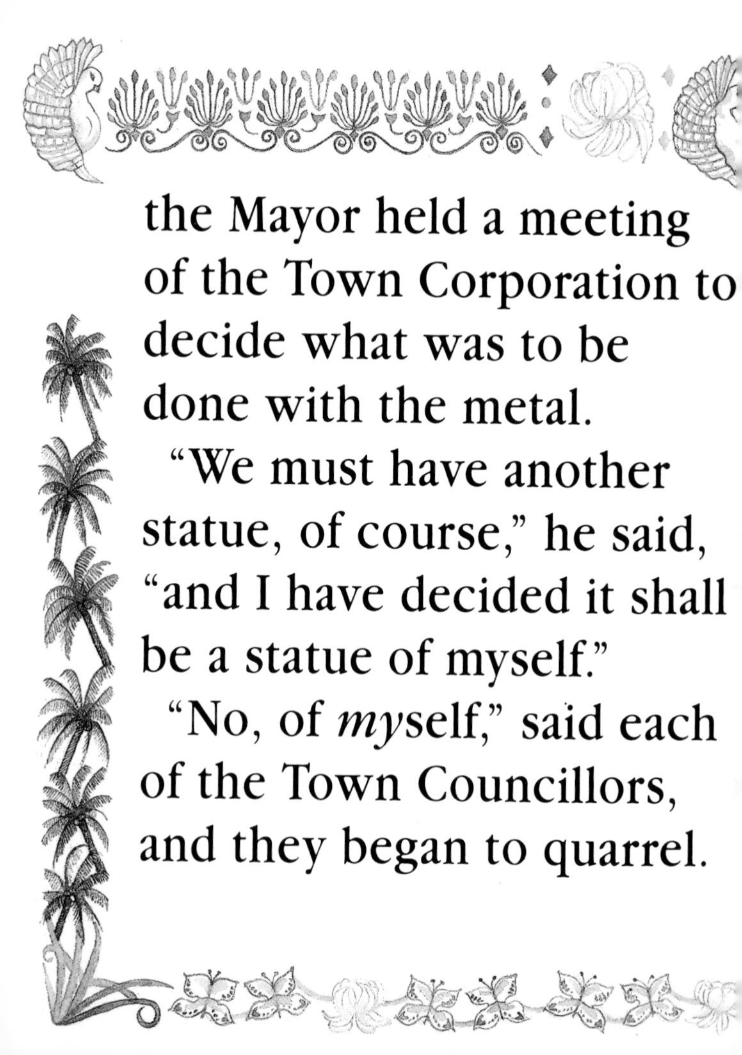

the Mayor held a meeting of the Town Corporation to decide what was to be done with the metal.

"We must have another statue, of course," he said, "and I have decided it shall be a statue of myself."

"No, of *my*self," said each of the Town Councillors, and they began to quarrel.

When I last heard of them they were quarrelling still.

"What a strange thing!" said the foreman of the workmen at the foundry. "This broken lead heart will not melt in the furnace. We must throw it away." So they threw it on a rubbish heap where the dead Swallow also lay.

"Bring Me the two most

precious things in the city," said God to one of His Angels and the Angel brought Him the leaden heart and the dead bird.

"You have chosen wisely," said God, "for in My garden of Paradise this little bird shall sing for evermore, and in My city of gold the Happy Prince shall praise Me."

The Remarkable Rocket

The King's son was going to be married so there was much rejoicing. He had waited a whole year for his bride, a Russian Princess, and at last she arrived in a sledge drawn by six reindeer. She wore a tiny cap of silver brocade on her head, a long ermine cloak and she was as pale as the Snow Palace in which she had lived.

"She is like a white rose!" cried the people as they threw flowers from the balconies.

At the gate of the castle the Prince was waiting to receive his beautiful bride. He was very handsome with dreamy violet eyes, and his hair shone like fine gold. When he saw the Princess he gently kissed her hand. "Your picture was indeed beautiful," he murmured, "but you are even more lovely than your picture," and the Princess blushed.

"She was like a white rose before," said a young page to his neighbour, "but now she looks like a red rose!" and the whole court was delighted.

After the splendid wedding ceremony there was a magnificent State Banquet which lasted for five hours. The Prince and Princess sat at the top of the Great Hall and drank out of a cup of clear crystal. Only true lovers could drink out of this cup, for if false lips touched it, it grew dull and cloudy.

"It is quite clear that they

love each other," said the little page. "It's as clear as crystal!" After the banquet there was a Grand Ball. The bride and bridegroom danced together, and the King insisted on playing the flute. He played very badly, but no-one dared to tell him so because he was King, and so they all cried out, "Charming! Quite charming!"

At midnight there was to be a grand firework display. The little Princess had never seen a firework in her life, so the King ordered the Royal Pyrotechnist to spare no cost and put on his best ever show for the day of her marriage.

"What are fireworks like?" the Princess asked late one evening as she was walking on the terrace.

"They are like the Aurora Borealis, the Northern Lights," replied the King, "only much more natural. In fact, I prefer them to the stars, for you always know when they are going to appear. They are as good as my own flute-playing."

The next day a great stand was set up in the King's garden and as soon as the Royal Pyrotechnist had put everything in its proper place ready for the grand display, the fireworks began to talk to each other.

"The world is certainly very beautiful," cried a little Squib. "Just look at those yellow tulips. Why, if they were real crackers

they could not be lovelier!"

"But not as lovely as the Princess," sighed the Catherine Wheel, and she remembered her lost love, an old wooden box who had meant a great deal to her in early life. "True love suffers and is silent," she continued. "I remember myself once — but no matter. Romance is a thing of the past."

"Nonsense!" said the Roman Candle. But the Catherine Wheel shook her head. "Romance is dead, Romance is dead, Romance is dead," she murmured. She was one of those people who think that if you say the same thing over and over a great many times it becomes true in the end. The Roman Candle drew himself up.

"Romance never dies," he said. "It is like the moon and lives for ever. The bride and bridegroom, for instance, love each other very dearly."

Suddenly a sharp, dry cough was heard and they all looked round.

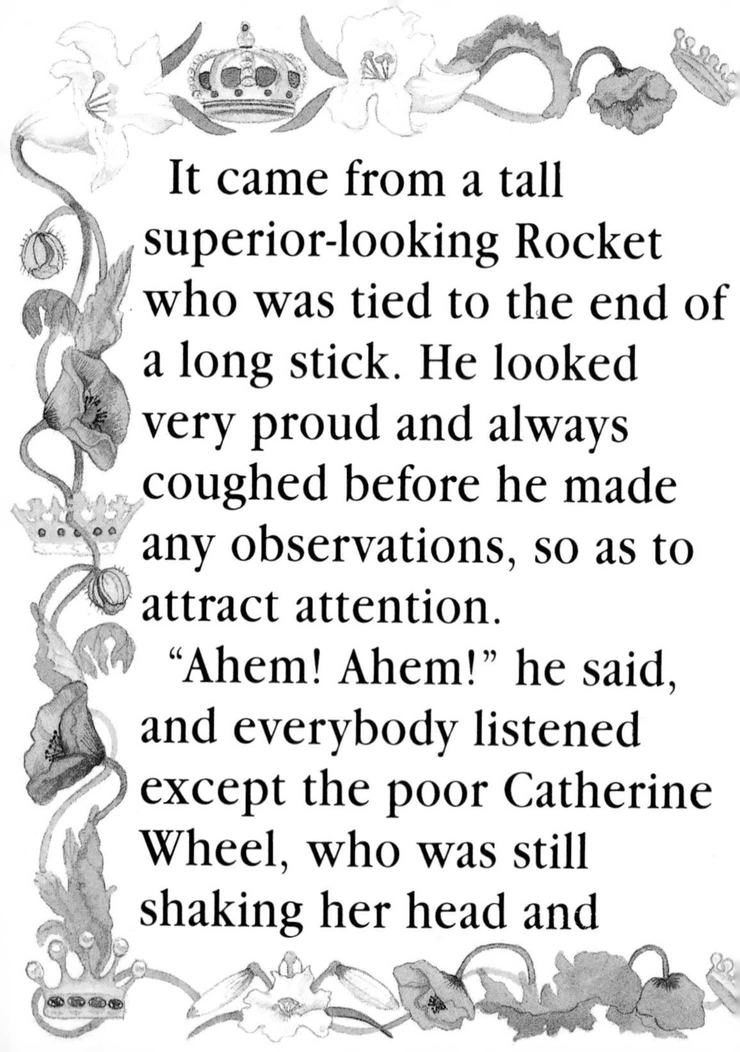

It came from a tall superior-looking Rocket who was tied to the end of a long stick. He looked very proud and always coughed before he made any observations, so as to attract attention.

"Ahem! Ahem!" he said, and everybody listened except the poor Catherine Wheel, who was still shaking her head and murmuring, "Romance is dead"

"How fortunate it is for the King's son," remarked the Rocket in a slow, important voice, "that he is to be married on the very day on which I am to be let off! Really, if it had not been arranged beforehand, it could not have turned out better for him — but Princes are always lucky."

"Dear me!" said the little Squib. "I thought it was quite the other way round and that we were to be let off in the Prince's honour."

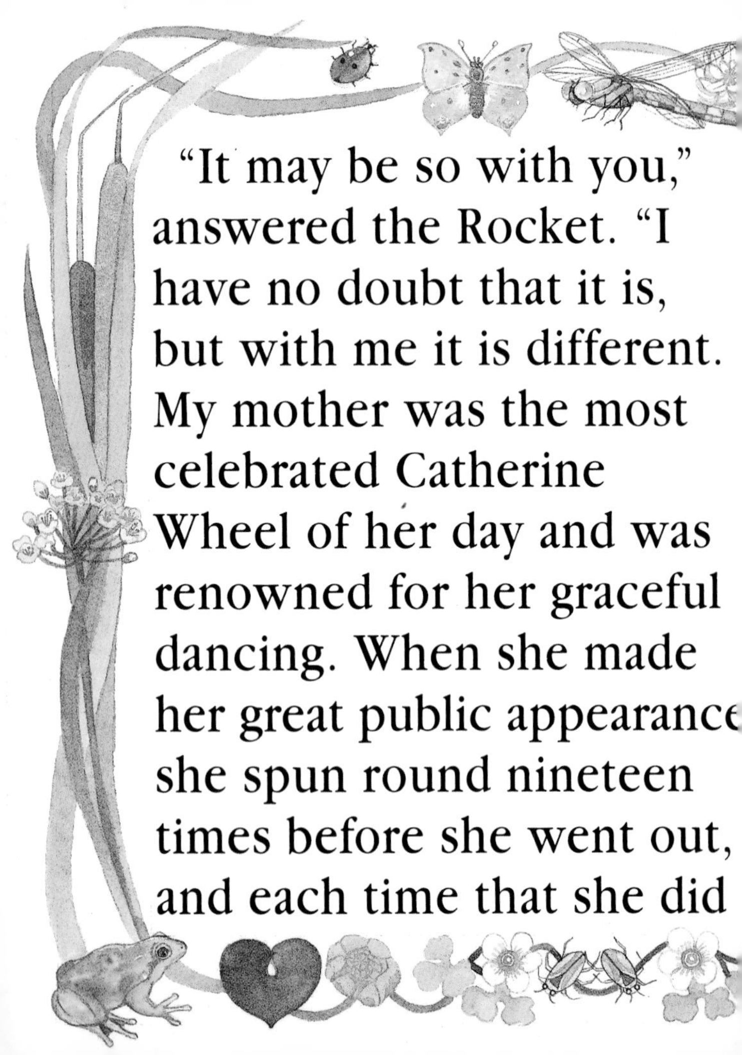

"It may be so with you," answered the Rocket. "I have no doubt that it is, but with me it is different. My mother was the most celebrated Catherine Wheel of her day and was renowned for her graceful dancing. When she made her great public appearance she spun round nineteen times before she went out, and each time that she did

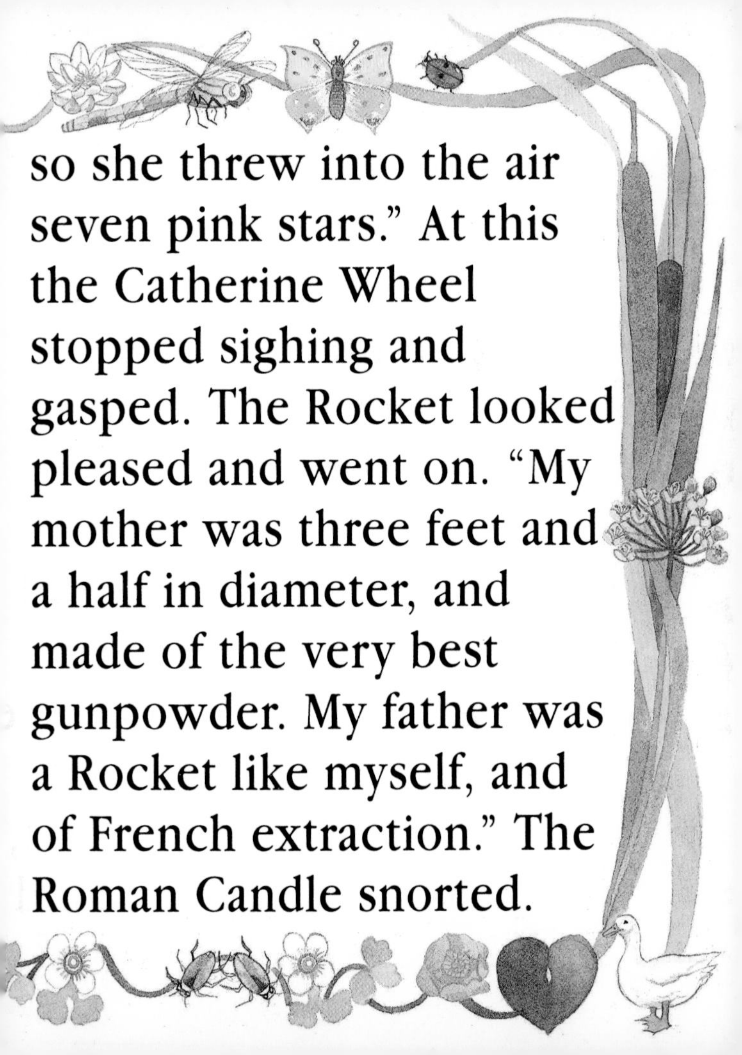

so she threw into the air seven pink stars." At this the Catherine Wheel stopped sighing and gasped. The Rocket looked pleased and went on. "My mother was three feet and a half in diameter, and made of the very best gunpowder. My father was a Rocket like myself, and of French extraction." The Roman Candle snorted.

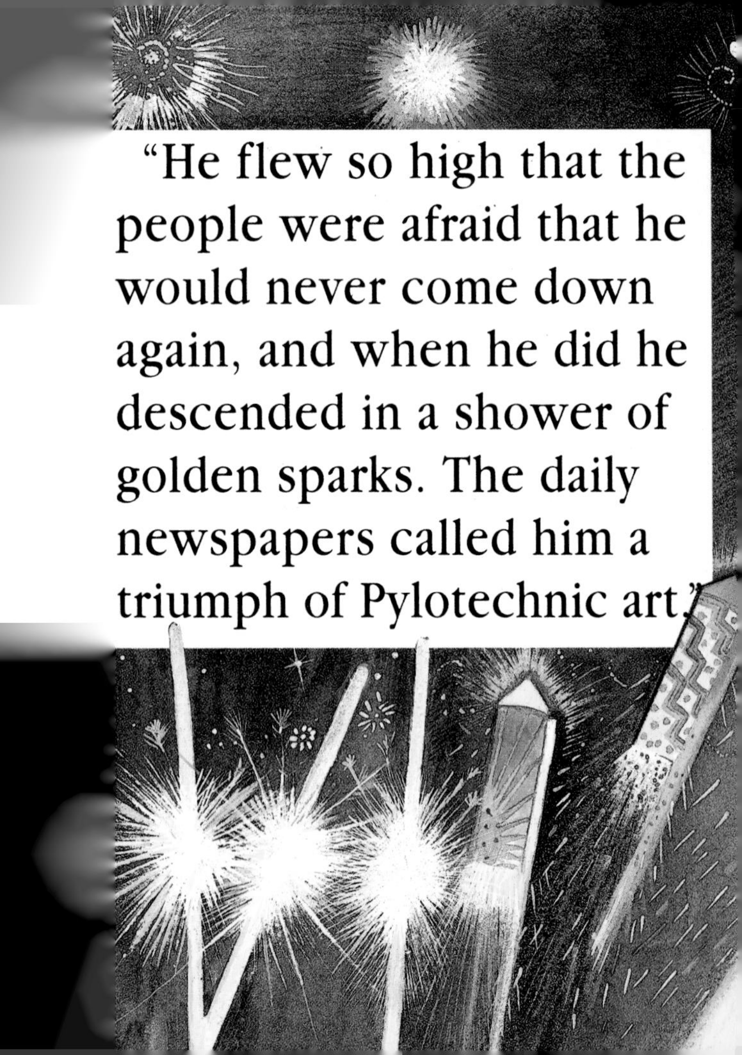

"He flew so high that the people were afraid that he would never come down again, and when he did he descended in a shower of golden sparks. The daily newspapers called him a triumph of Pylotechnic art."

"*Pyro*technic, you mean," said a Bengal Light. "I know it is Pyrotechnic for I saw it written on my own canister."

"Well, *I* said Pylotechnic," answered the Rocket in a severe tone of voice, and the Bengal Light felt so crushed that he began to bully the little squibs in order to show that he was still a person of some

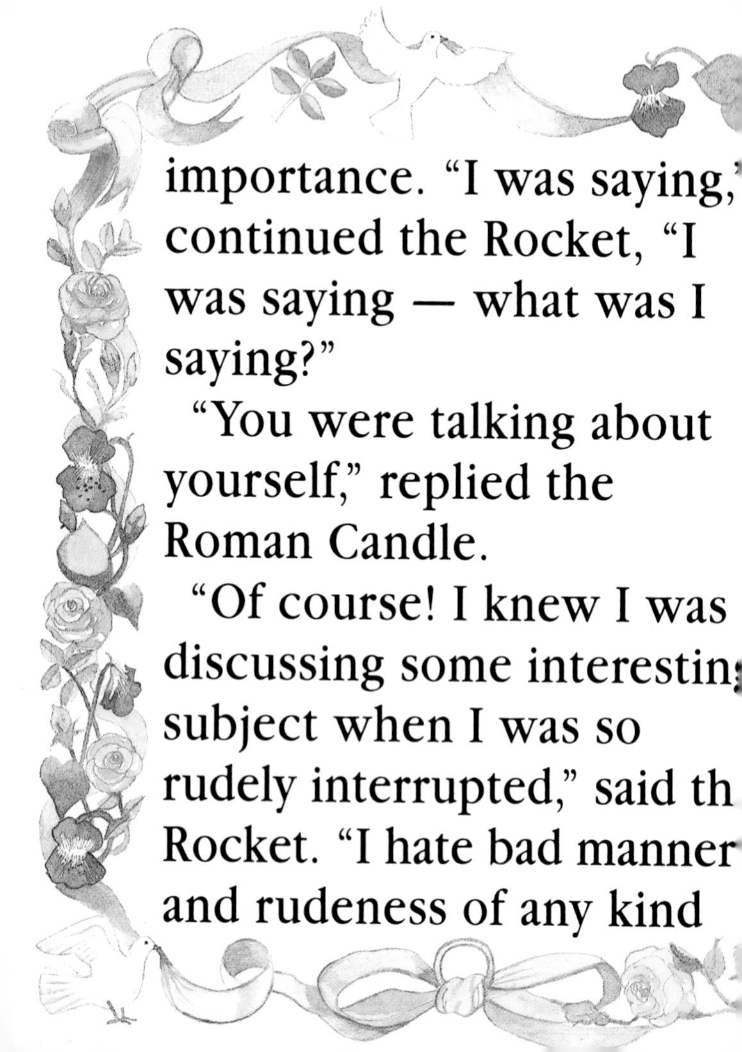

importance. "I was saying,"
continued the Rocket, "I
was saying — what was I
saying?"

"You were talking about
yourself," replied the
Roman Candle.

"Of course! I knew I was
discussing some interesting
subject when I was so
rudely interrupted," said the
Rocket. "I hate bad manners
and rudeness of any kind

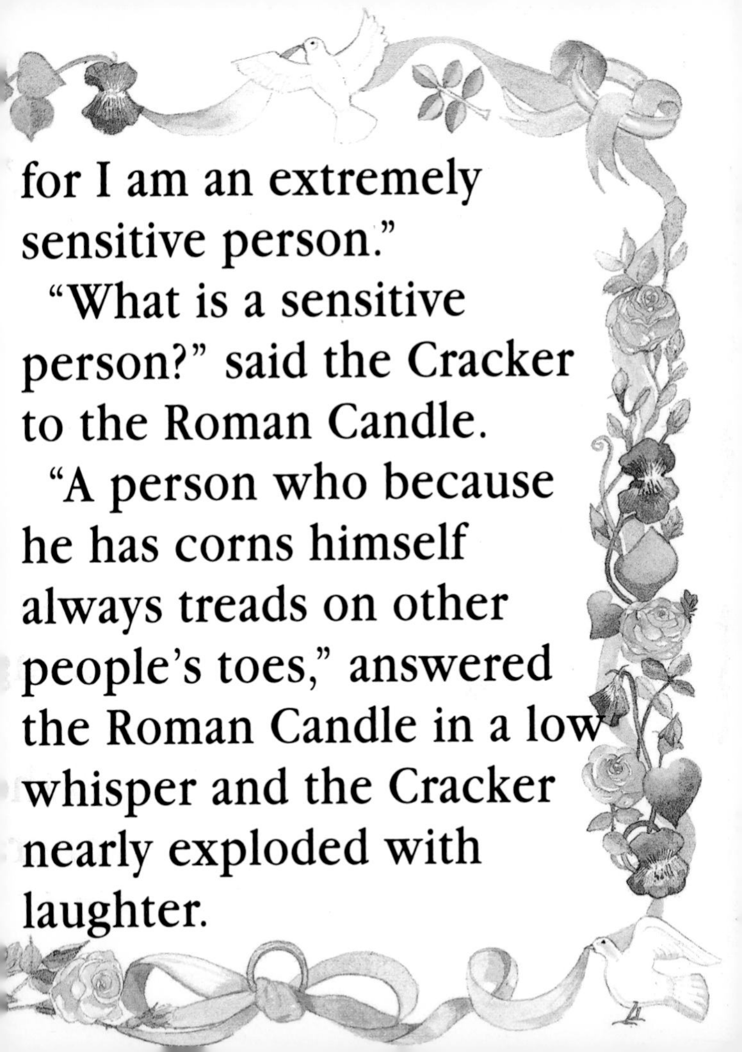

for I am an extremely sensitive person."

"What is a sensitive person?" said the Cracker to the Roman Candle.

"A person who because he has corns himself always treads on other people's toes," answered the Roman Candle in a low whisper and the Cracker nearly exploded with laughter.

"Pray, what are you laughing at?" inquired the Rocket. "*I* am not laughing."

"I am laughing because I am happy," replied the Firecracker.

"That is a very selfish reason," said the Rocket angrily. "What right have you to be happy? You should be thinking about the others. In fact, you should be thinking about me. I am always thinking about myself, and I expect everybody else to do the same thing. Really, when I begin to reflect on the importance of my position,

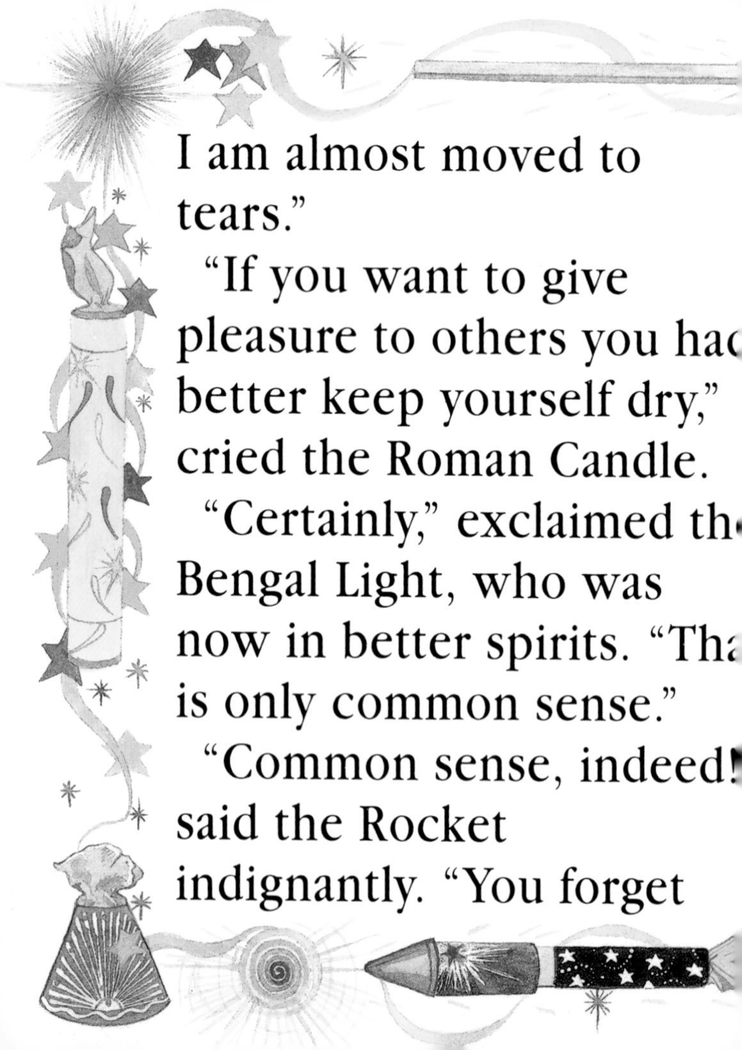

I am almost moved to
tears."

"If you want to give
pleasure to others you had
better keep yourself dry,"
cried the Roman Candle.

"Certainly," exclaimed the
Bengal Light, who was
now in better spirits. "That
is only common sense."

"Common sense, indeed!"
said the Rocket
indignantly. "You forget

that I am very uncommon, and very remarkable. Why, anybody can have common sense, but I have a vivid imagination and an emotional nature. Fortunately for myself, I don't care. The only thing that keeps me going is the knowledge that I am better than everybody else. But none of you have any hearts," he complained.

"Here you are laughing and making merry just as if the Prince and Princess had not just been married," and the Rocket shook his head sorrowfully.

"Well, really," exclaimed a small Fire-balloon, "and why not? It is a most joyful occasion, and when I soar up into the air I intend to tell the stars all about it. You will see them all twinkle when I describe the pretty bride."

"Ah! what a trivial view of life!" said the Rocket, "but it is only what I have come to expect of you."

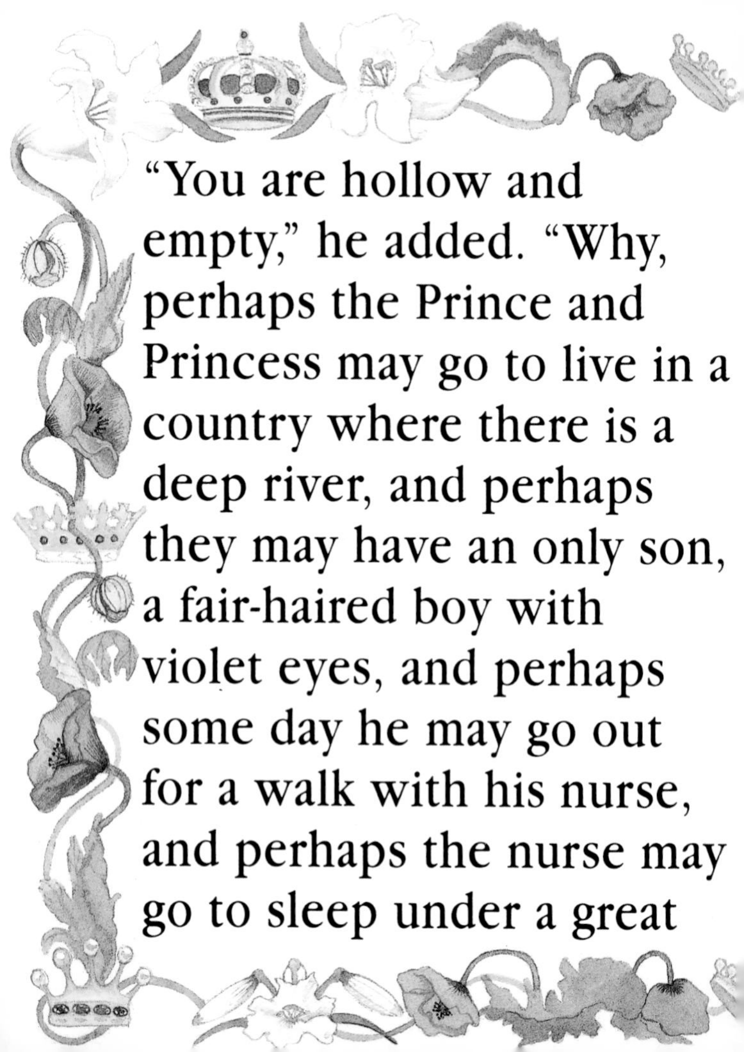

"You are hollow and empty," he added. "Why, perhaps the Prince and Princess may go to live in a country where there is a deep river, and perhaps they may have an only son, a fair-haired boy with violet eyes, and perhaps some day he may go out for a walk with his nurse, and perhaps the nurse may go to sleep under a great elder-tree, and perhaps the little boy may fall into the deep river and be drowned. What a terrible misfortune! Poor people, to lose their only son! It is really too dreadful! I shall never get over it."

"But they have *not* lost their only son," said the Roman Candle. "No misfortune has happened to them at all."

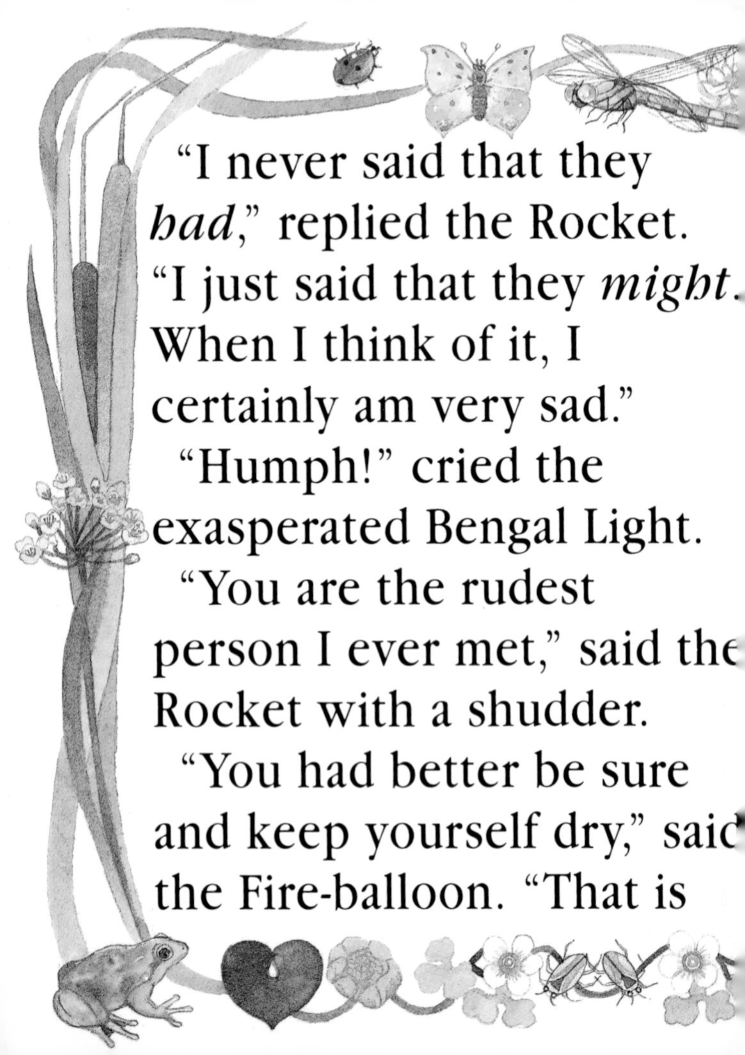

"I never said that they *had*," replied the Rocket. "I just said that they *might*. When I think of it, I certainly am very sad."

"Humph!" cried the exasperated Bengal Light.

"You are the rudest person I ever met," said the Rocket with a shudder.

"You had better be sure and keep yourself dry," said the Fire-balloon. "That is

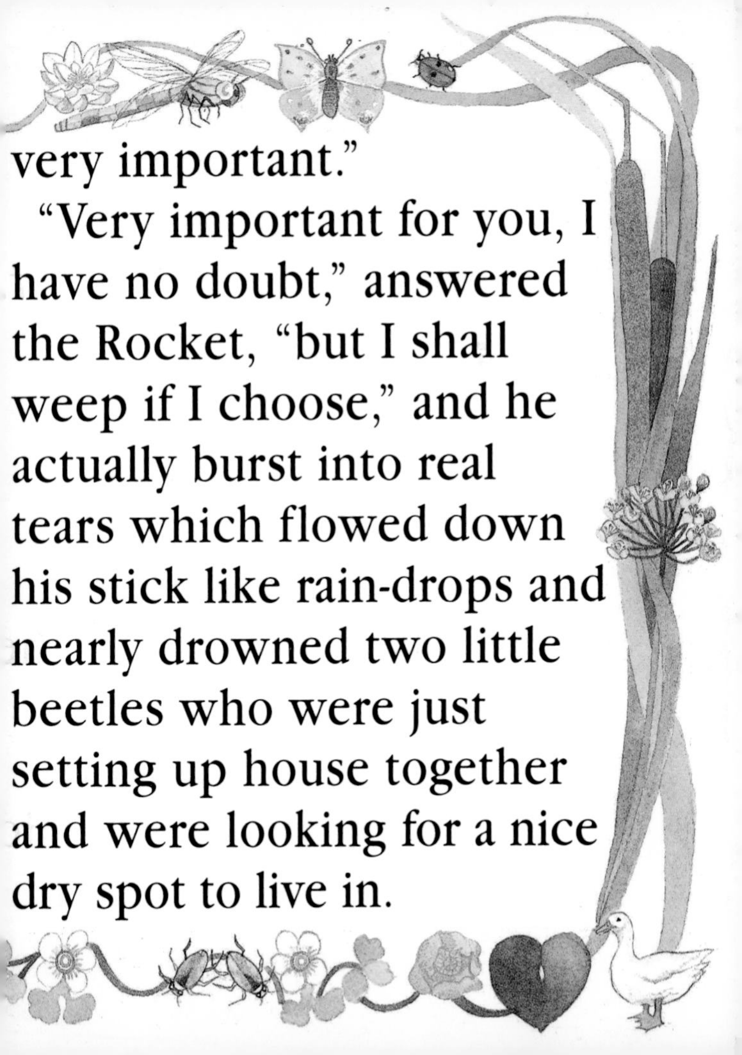

very important."

"Very important for you, I have no doubt," answered the Rocket, "but I shall weep if I choose," and he actually burst into real tears which flowed down his stick like rain-drops and nearly drowned two little beetles who were just setting up house together and were looking for a nice dry spot to live in.

The Roman Candle and the Bengal Light were quite indignant, and kept saying, "Humbug! Humbug!" at the top of their voices.

Then the moon rose in the night sky like a wonderful silver shield and the stars began to shine and the sound of music came from the palace. The Prince and Princess were dancing arm in arm.

They danced so very beautifully that the tall white lilies peeped in at the window to watch, and the great red poppies nodded their heads in time to the music.

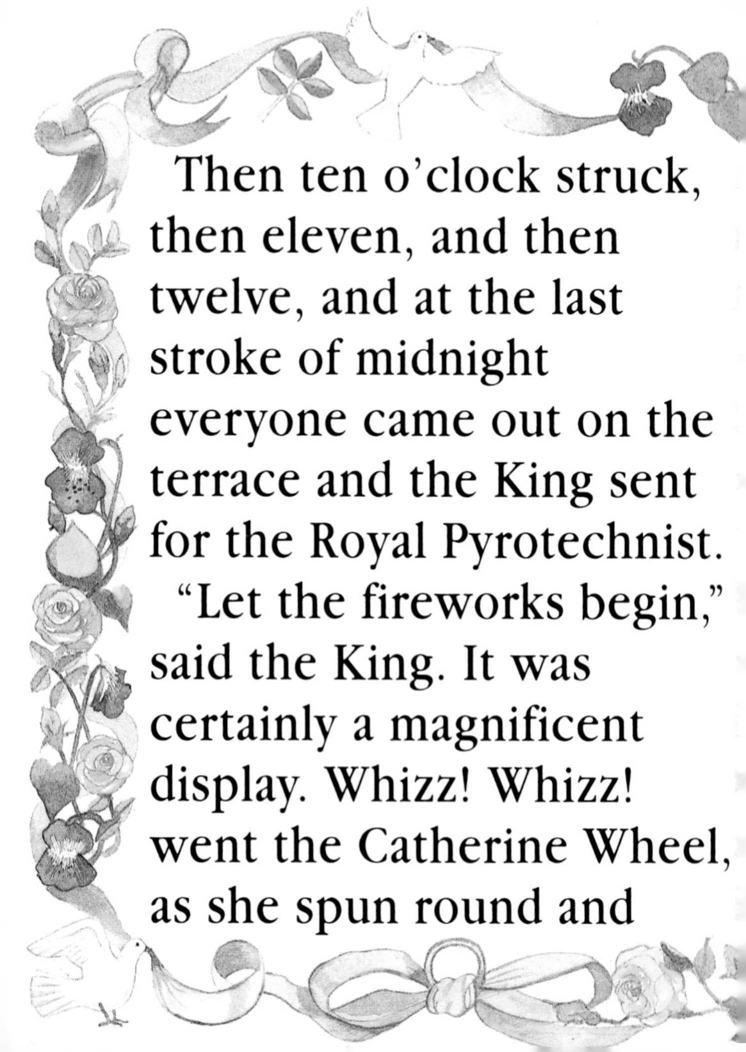

Then ten o'clock struck, then eleven, and then twelve, and at the last stroke of midnight everyone came out on the terrace and the King sent for the Royal Pyrotechnist.

"Let the fireworks begin," said the King. It was certainly a magnificent display. Whizz! Whizz! went the Catherine Wheel, as she spun round and

round. Boom! Boom! went the Roman Candle. Then the Squibs danced all over the place, and the Bengal Lights made everything look scarlet. "Goodbye," cried the Fire-balloon, as he soared away, dropping tiny blue sparks. Bang! Bang! answered the Crackers, who were enjoying themselves immensely.

Everyone was a great success except the Remarkable Rocket. He was so damp with crying that he could not go off at all. His gunpowder was so wet with tears that it was no use whatever.

All the other fireworks shot up into the sky like wonderful golden flowers with blossoms of fire. Hurray! Hurray! cried the courtiers, and the little Princess laughed with pleasure.

"I suppose they are reserving me for some grand occasion," said the Rocket and he looked more superior than ever.

The next day the workmen came to tidy up. "They have come for me," said the Rocket, and he put his nose in the air, and began to frown severely, as if he were thinking about some very important subject. But they took no notice of him at all until they were leaving. Then one of them bent down and picked him up.

"What a bad rocket!" he cried and threw him over the wall into the ditch.

"*Bad* Rocket? *Bad* Rocket?" said the Rocket, as he whirled through the air. "Impossible! *Grand* Rocket, that is what the man said. Bad and Grand sound very much the same, indeed they often are the same," and with that he fell into the mud.

"It is not comfortable here," he remarked, "but no doubt it is some fashionable holiday resort, and they have sent me away to regain my health. I could certainly do with the rest." Then a little Frog with bright jewelled eyes and a green mottled coat swam up to him. "A new arrival, I see!" said the Frog. "Well, after all, there is nothing like mud. Give me rainy weather and a ditch, and I am quite happy!" "Ahem! Ahem!" said the Rocket, and he began to cough. "What a delightful voice you have!" cried the Frog. "Really it is quite like a croak, and croaking is, of course, the most musical sound in the world. You will hear us all this evening. We sit in the old duck-pond close by the farmer's house, and as soon as the moon rises we begin. It is so entrancing that everybody lies awake to listen to us. In fact, it was only yesterday that I heard the farmer's wife say to her mother that she could not get a wink of sleep at night on account of us. It is most pleasing to find oneself so popular."

"Ahem! Ahem!" said the Rocket angrily. He was very much annoyed that he couldn't get a word in.

"I hope you will come over to the duck-pond," continued the Frog. "I am off to look for my six beautiful daughters. I am so afraid the Pike may meet them. He is a perfect monster, and would have no hesitation in eating

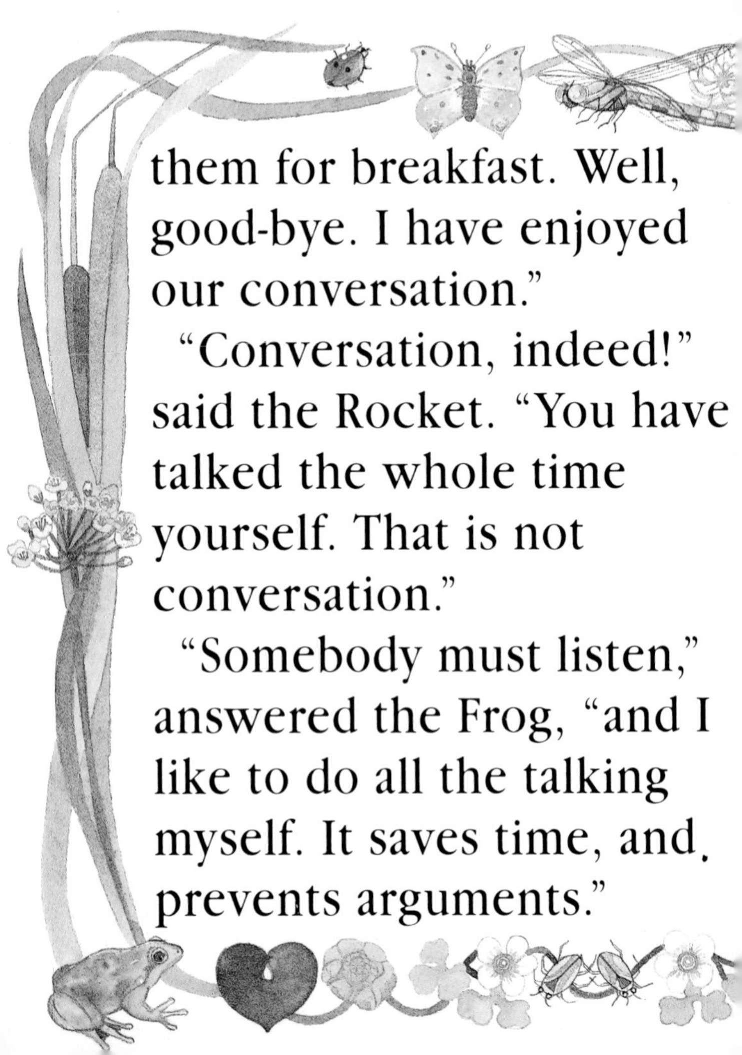

them for breakfast. Well, good-bye. I have enjoyed our conversation."

"Conversation, indeed!" said the Rocket. "You have talked the whole time yourself. That is not conversation."

"Somebody must listen," answered the Frog, "and I like to do all the talking myself. It saves time, and prevents arguments."

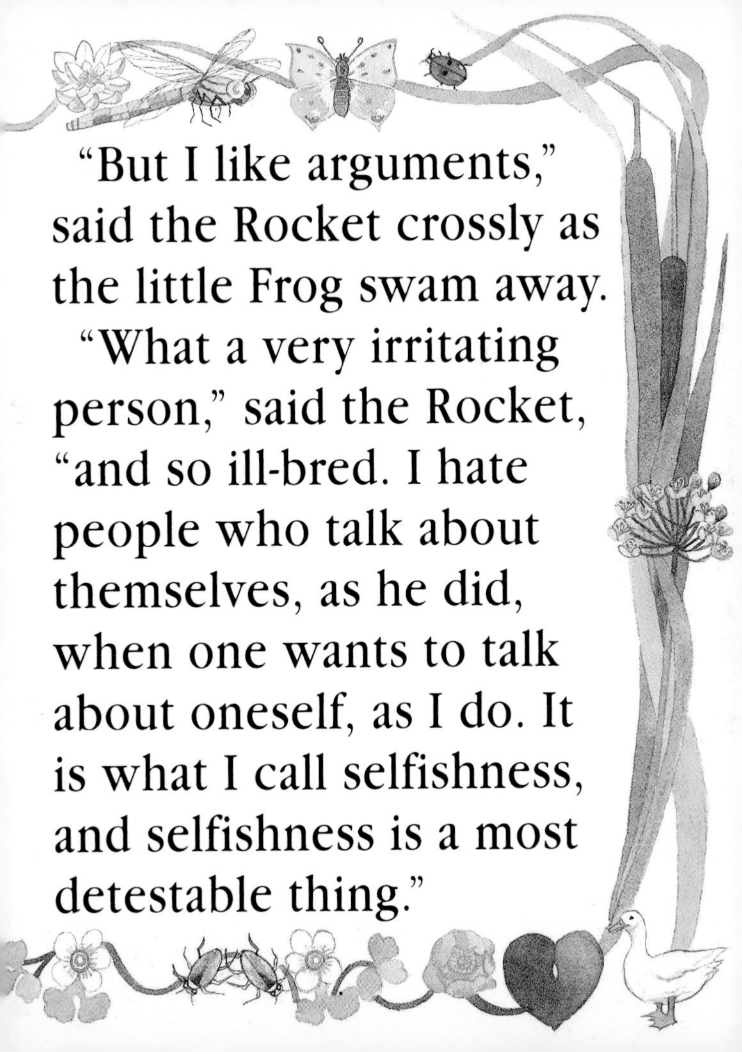

"But I like arguments," said the Rocket crossly as the little Frog swam away. "What a very irritating person," said the Rocket, "and so ill-bred. I hate people who talk about themselves, as he did, when one wants to talk about oneself, as I do. It is what I call selfishness, and selfishness is a most detestable thing."

"It is no good talking to him," said a Dragonfly, who was sitting on top of a large brown bulrush. "No good at all, for he has gone away and can't hear you."

"Well, that is his loss, not mine," answered the Rocket. "I am not going to stop talking to him merely because he pays no attention. I like hearing myself talk. It is one of my greatest pleasures. I often have long conversations all by myself, and I am so clever that sometimes I don't understand a single word of what I am saying."

"Humph!" said the Dragonfly, and he spread a pair of lovely gauze wings and soared away.

"How very silly of him not to stay here and listen to me!" said the Rocket. "However, I don't care a bit. Genius like mine is sure to be appreciated some day," and he sank down a little deeper into the mud.

After some time a large White Duck swam up to him. She had yellow legs and webbed feet, and was considered a great beauty on account of her magnificent waddle.

"Quack, quack, quack," she said. "What a curious shape you are! May I ask were you born like that, or is it the result of an accident?"

"I can't expect other people to be as remarkable as me," said the Rocket. "You will no doubt be

surprised to hear that I can fly up into the sky, and come down in a shower of golden sparks."

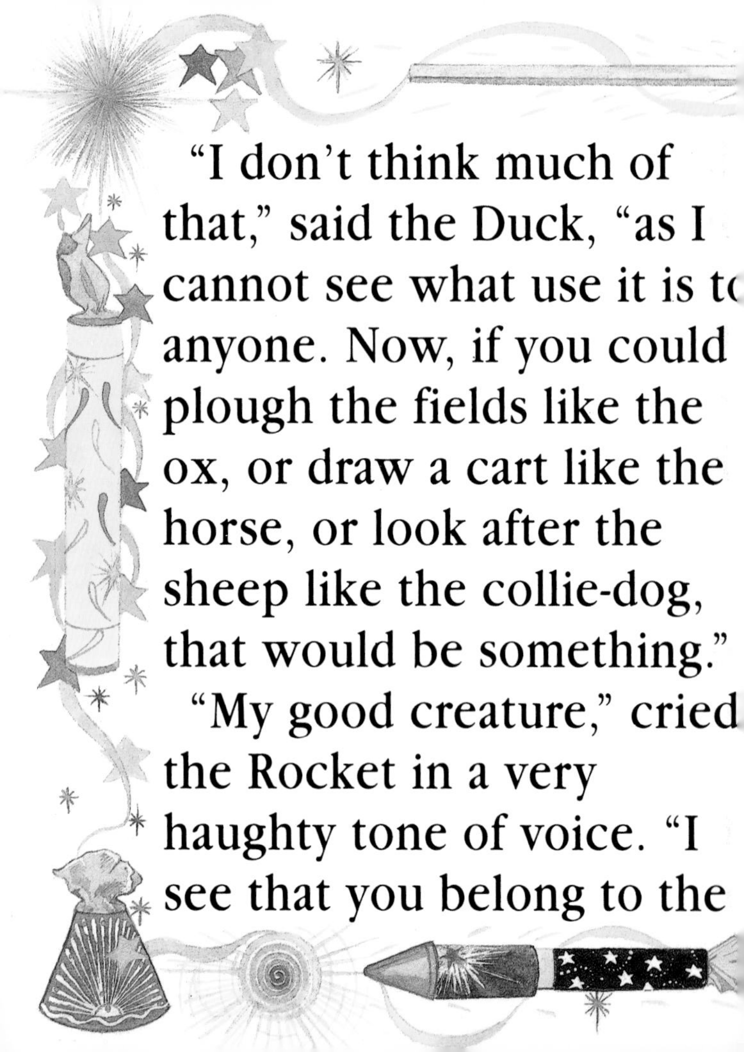

"I don't think much of that," said the Duck, "as I cannot see what use it is to anyone. Now, if you could plough the fields like the ox, or draw a cart like the horse, or look after the sheep like the collie-dog, that would be something."

"My good creature," cried the Rocket in a very haughty tone of voice. "I see that you belong to the

lower orders. A person of my position is never useful. We don't work. I believe that people only work hard because they have nothing better to do."

"Well, well," said the Duck, who was of a very peaceful disposition, and never quarrelled with anyone, "everybody is entitled to their own opinion. Are you moving here?"

"Oh! dear no," cried the Rocket. "I am merely a visitor, a distinguished visitor. The fact is that I find the place rather tedious. I shall probably go back to Court, for I know that I am destined to make a sensation in the world."

"I go in for home life and look after my family," replied the Duck.

"I am made for public life," said the Rocket, "and so are all my relations, even the humblest of them. Whenever we appear we cause great excitement." Then the White Duck swam away down the stream, saying, "Quack, quack, quack."

"Come back! Come back!" screamed the Rocket. "I still have a great deal to say to you." Then he sank a little deeper still into the mud, and began to think about the loneliness of genius. Suddenly two little boys in brown caps came running down the bank with a kettle and some twigs.

"They must be coming for

me," said the Rocket, and he tried to look very dignified.

"Hallo!" cried one of the boys, "look at this old stick! I wonder how it got here," and he picked the rocket out of the ditch.

"*Old* Stick!" said the Rocket. "Impossible! *Gold* Stick, that is what he said. Gold Stick is very complimentary."

"Let us put it on our fire!" said the other boy. "It should burn well and will help to boil the kettle more quickly."

So they piled the twigs together, put the Rocket on top, and lit the fire.

"This is magnificent," cried the Rocket. "They are going to let me off in broad daylight, so that everyone can see me."

"Let's go to sleep now," said the boys, "and when we wake up the kettle will be boiled," and they lay down on the grass.

The Rocket was very damp so he took a long time to burn but at last the fire caught him.

"Now I am going off!" he cried, and he stood up ramrod stiff on his stick and held himself very tall

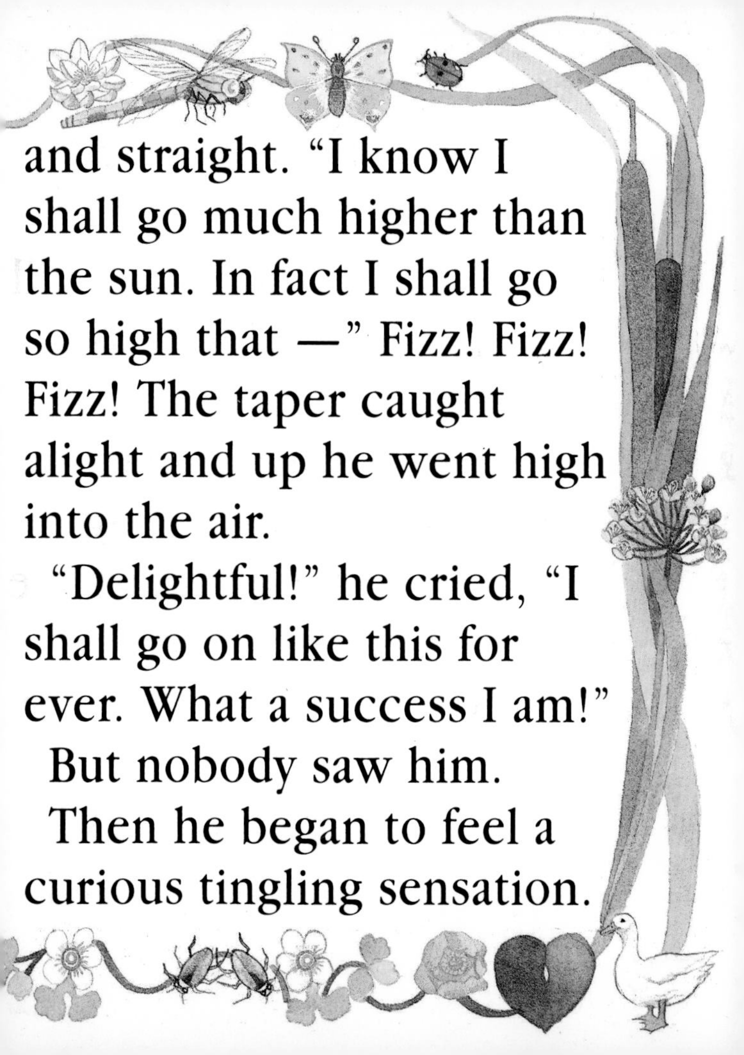

and straight. "I know I shall go much higher than the sun. In fact I shall go so high that —" Fizz! Fizz! Fizz! The taper caught alight and up he went high into the air.

"Delightful!" he cried, "I shall go on like this for ever. What a success I am!"

But nobody saw him.

Then he began to feel a curious tingling sensation.

"Now I am going to explode," he cried. "I shall set the whole world on fire, and make such a noise that nobody will talk about anything else for a whole year." And he certainly did explode. Bang! Bang! Bang! went the gunpowder.

There was no doubt about it, he certainly exploded in a marvellous shower of golden sparks.

But nobody heard him, not even the two little boys for they were sound asleep. Then all that was left of him was the stick, and it fell down on the back of a goose who was taking a walk by the side of the ditch.

"Good heavens!" cried the Goose. "It is raining sticks!" and she carefully smoothed her feathers.

"I knew I should create a great sensation," gasped the Rocket — and that was the end of him.